ONE
BLINK
AT A TIME

Ismail and Cheryl Tsieprati

⟨ **W9-APH-325**

Kindle edition is now available

Includes live web links to helpful resources and critical glossary terms

One Blink at a Time is an upbeat, inspiring story of love, courage, and optimism. Ismail and Cheryl Tsieprati recount in alternating chapters how they deal with their daily challenges living for 30 years with ALS (Amyotrophic Lateral Sclerosis, also known as Lou Gehrig's Disease). Although ALS has left him paralyzed and unable to breathe without the help of a ventilator, Ismail continues to live a happy and productive life.

Go to **oneblinkatatime.com** to order both soft cover and Kindle editions or to learn more. Volume discounts are available. A portion of the proceeds from the sales of *One Blink at a Time* will be donated to The ALS Association.

Praise for
One Blink at a Time...

This is the remarkable story of Cheryl and Ismail's resourceful-
ness and creativity in preserving Ismail's ability to lead a
satisfying and productive life and to communicate with the world
around him despite total paralysis from advanced ALS. Their
interest in the use of computer and assistive devices as well as
their exploration of potential benefits of new technologies and
research, including a project that rewires cockroach brains, is
amazing. I strongly recommend this book.

—Rebecca A. Hanson, M.D. Clinical
Professor in Pediatric Neurology and
Orthopedics (Cerebral Palsy), UCLA

I was fortunate to receive an advance copy of this book. What a
terrific read...detailed, honest and poignant. I found myself at
various times in tears, laughing out loud, and getting goose
bumps. Mostly I found myself inspired by the ways these two
talented, charismatic individuals rose above every challenge and
continue to live an amazing and full life together. As I finished
the last page a favorite quote by Albert Camus came to my mind:
"in the depths of winter I found in me an invincible summer."
Thank you Ismail and Cheryl for the invincible summers inside
you and for reminding us of the power of love. You may have
ALS, but ALS does not have you!

—Richard Bedlack, M.D., Ph.D.
Director of Duke University
ALS Clinic , Durham, NC

With inspiration and love, Ismail and Cheryl Tsieprati have shared the writing of this book as they have shared all the joys, challenges, hopes and dreams of their life together and with Ismail's 30-year journey with ALS. They have educated all of us, in a very personal and individual way, about how to cope and live a high quality of life with ALS with the help and support of friends, family and community resources. Extraordinary personal experiences combined with a glossary of ALS-related definitions and a list of helpful community resources comprise a most helpful, meaningful and worthwhile read.

— Madelon Thomson, LCSW
Director of Care Services,
ALS Association
Golden West Chapter

**Life
is a
Celebration!**

Ismail

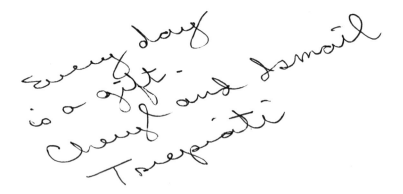

ONE
BLINK
AT A TIME

Ismail and Cheryl Tsieprati

ISBN 978-1-883423-37-7

First Edition
10 9 8 7 6 5 4 3 2 1

Cover & Book Design by Cathy Feldman

Book Production by Blue Point Books

Photography Credits:
Cecilia Chacon: Cover
Picture People, Simi Valley, CA: Page 3
Phil Gries: Pages 5, 12, 47, 158, 161
Jean Sardou Portrait Studio: Page 8
Lynn Klein: Page 17

To order this book in quantity for your organization please contact:
Blue Point Books
bpbooks@west.net • 800-858-1058

Published by Blue Point Books
P.O. Box 91347
Santa Barbara, CA 93190-1347
www.bluepointbooks.com

Printed in United States of America

Introduction

When I read *One Blink at a Time*, I felt like I was on the journey with Ismail and Cheryl. My first reaction was WOW! The emotion, the rawness of the journey, the sharing of lessons learned and how it can help others on many levels was incredible. I cannot say enough about how connected I felt to them as I read it.

Their love of life and for each other as they bravely fight this disease and constantly adjust to their new normal is a life lesson for all, not just those families that have been impacted by ALS.

After reading their book I am speechless. I thought I understood what it was like to have ALS and how it affects individuals and families. Now I know that my experience just scratched the surface. Ismail's and Cheryl's story has touched my heart and soul and reminds me why the advocacy work that we do for the ALS community is so crucial.

Ismail and Cheryl have opened up their lives and hearts to the world through this book, and the world will be better for reading it.

Ted Harada
ALS patient & advocate
Member, ALS Association
National Board of Trustees

Foreword

This memoir, *One Blink at a Time,* is like no other book ever written about Amyotrophic Lateral Sclerosis (ALS, or Lou Gehrig's Disease). Other fictional and non-fictional accounts related to challenges encountered with ALS have been written over the years, but no other book spans a 30-year retrospective on the challenges endured by both the primary caregiver and the person diagnosed with ALS.

This book is a love story that transcends all love stories. When asked how she has made it through 30 years of being a caregiver for her husband, Cheryl says "I have made it because Ismail, despite his illness, the pain he suffers every day, and his physical limitations, continues to enjoy life and be upbeat, good-natured, and loving. Ismail and I have as much respect and affection for one another as we did the day we were married."

My brotherhood with Ismail spans 52 years. I first met him in September, 1962, our first night at City College of New York and our first film class together. Our friendship grew. We worked on mutual films and learned filmmaking by experimenting. We even acted in each other's film projects. Some of these early 8mm & 16mm black and white films still survive.

In 1965, Ismail moved to Los Angeles to find work. I followed in January, 1966, where I was accepted to the U.C.L.A. graduate program in Theater Arts. Ismail and I lived together for almost two years in a small studio apartment in Beverly Hills. The rent was $110 a month, split two ways! Although neither of us had a car, we both enjoyed bachelorhood nonetheless. It was an innocent time I always reflect upon with fond memories of living our dreams of seeking acceptance and advancement in the motion picture industry.

In June of 1967, I returned to New York where I taught elementary school in Harlem for three years. Ismail continued to live in West Hollywood, working at a film stock library house and producing educational films. He continued to write movie scripts and look for directing opportunities. During this time, we spoke by phone and wrote to one another, staying in touch.

In 1970, my wife Jane and I returned to Los Angeles. We lived in West Hollywood five minutes away from Ismail. He was dating Cheryl at the time. On November 26, 1970, I drove both of them to Las Vegas, where they were married. Jane was the bridesmaid. I was the best man, the photographer, and the chauffer. We were the entire wedding party! We knew on that wedding day that Cheryl and Ismail shared an extraordinary bond.

I am overwhelmed by Ismail's and Cheryl's journey but not one bit surprised that they are more in love today than when they got married in 1970!

Their story reveals one of life's amazing universal lessons. They have, together and separately, successfully encountered challenges that most people have never experienced. In telling their many episodes of drama, revelation, and insight, spanning more than 11,000 days, what is instilled in the reader is the profundity of what you and I are capable of accomplishing in life, that ALL IS POSSIBLE, even during the most horrific circumstances, if our motivation and aspirations remain strong.

"ALS has robbed me of my ability to move my body," Ismail states, "but it will never take away my feelings or my dreams...Cheryl and I will continue dreaming as long as we live. ALS will never take that away from me."

I feel good being around Ismail and Cheryl. They uplift me. Their attitude and approach to living as normal a life as possible impresses me. I admire Ismail's optimism and constant verve for living and working, his constant smiling face and laughter, his inner confidence. Cheryl's love and devotion to Ismail is prolific. She is totally supportive and protective of his needs. She is his lifeline that allows Ismail to live creatively and with dignity.

Defying odds by a thousand fold, created by so many factors that happen rarely in a lifetime, Ismail and Cheryl embarked on a personal journey that would in all probability be a difficult voyage filled with uncertainty and the unexpected, but navigated with one focus — to live, and to make one's days, weeks, months, years, decades meaningful and happy. They have been an inspiration to all who have been in their presence. This memoir allows many others to experience their exceptional and revealing journey…one that has astounded me every single day for the past 30 years.

Phil Gries
Sea Cliff, New York
September 2014

Dedication

This book is dedicated to people everywhere who are living with ALS or other life-altering conditions. May they face every challenge with courage and live every day with unwavering optimism, determination, and hope.

Contents

ONE
BLINK
AT A TIME

Our Unexpected Journey

Cheryl and Ismail

Ismail and I have been married for 44 years. Like all married couples, we have been through a lot together — times of big dreams, times of dashed hopes. Life has taken us on a journey we never expected and for which we never could have planned.

Ismail, a man who had always been strong, vibrant, and energetic, began to experience pain and weakness in his right arm. The weakness worsened and began to spread. He began to have difficulty doing yard work, cleaning his lawnmower, dressing himself. Then came the dreaded diagnosis: Amyotrophic Lateral Sclerosis (ALS). Lou Gehrig's disease. Progressive. Incurable. Most people with ALS die within two to five years of diagnosis. Not Ismail. "Don't worry," he told me when we first learned of his diagnosis. "I'm very strong."

Those words, spoken with undaunted optimism and determination, broke my heart. From all I had heard about ALS I believed that his situation was hopeless. He would grow progressively weaker no matter how hard he tried to fight. He would die young. Still, we made a pact. We would fight this battle together, do whatever we could to beat the odds and keep Ismail alive and happy for as long as we could.

Since Ismail's disease had been progressing slowly to that point, our hope was that he would live at least another ten years. Ten years! If only we could be lucky enough to have ten more years together!

To everyone's surprise, Ismail is still alive today and enjoying excellent quality of life, thirty years after his ALS symptoms began.

Our journey has been challenging, surprising, and at times, heart-breaking as ALS crept persistently through Ismail's body. Although the disease has robbed him of his ability to speak, Ismail has not let it silence him. He continues to spell out words by selecting alphabet letters on a chart one eye blink at a time. Our love and dedication to one another has continued to grow stronger; our determination remains unbroken; our hopes and dreams stubbornly bright. We have survived the years and the losses they have brought by facing them one day, one blink at a time.

Facing Bad News

Ismail in 1989

For more than fifteen years I worked in film and video. Then, as luck would have it, an incurable disease, ALS, began to paralyze me and eventually took away the most precious thing to any human being — my means of communication. Speech.

The first thing I experienced was pain in my right arm, my right thumb, and my neck. The pain came and went. As far back as the late 1960s, a doctor prescribed a neck collar for me to use while I worked. I began to experience weakness in my right arm in 1976. By 1980, I was unable to hold my niece Lindsay, then a baby, in my right arm. A doctor told me it was nothing but a pinched nerve. He suggested I take Tylenol. Discouraged, still in pain, I returned home. The pain continued to increase. Later, I discovered that I had lost muscle between my thumb and index finger. This change scared me. I made an appointment with a different doctor. He suggested I practice squeezing a soft rubber ball to build up the muscle and prescribed a neck brace. I returned home with a big hope that this would solve my problem. My friend Phil Gries remembers seeing me squeezing a ball when he came out from New York for a visit on December 26, 1983.

As time went on, my problem got worse. I made another appointment with the same doctor. After he examined me, he sent me to a neurosurgeon. The neurosurgeon checked my hand and told me he would operate on my thumb, but he wasn't sure the operation would help.

During an annual physical examination, my family doctor happened to notice twitching in my breast. He asked me how long I had been feeling the twitching. I told him I didn't know. He sent me to see a neurologist.

Dr. Rebecca Hanson was not only a great doctor, but she was also the head of the neurology department. She gave me a very thorough examination. While examining me, she discovered a twitching and a weakness of control of my tongue. She tested the strength of my tongue by having me push it against the inside of my cheek while she pushed back on the outside of my cheek with her hand. Afterwards, she sent me for an electromyogram (EMG), a test that checks muscles and the nerves that control muscles. Needles were put in my tongue. The needles were attached by wires to an electrical recorder. The test was very painful. After Dr. Hanson got the test results, she called Cheryl at home and asked her to come in to the office. She wanted to talk to both of us together about her diagnosis.

She gave us the bad news. I had ALS. She explained what would happen and described the disease. She told us how ALS kills a human being by destroying nerve cells that allow the brain to control muscle movement. Eventually, the person becomes paralyzed. The muscles of the diaphragm stop working, causing respiratory failure. She told us how long I was expected to live: two to five years is the average for most people. She assured us, however, that mine seemed to be a slower progressing form of the disease.

I did not expect this news. I did not know about this disease. Even though Dr. Hanson was certain of her diagnosis, she suggested that I see Dr. W. King Engel, Director of the USC Neuromuscular Center at the Good Samaritan Hospital, for a second opinion. Dr. Engel is a world-renowned specialist in neuromuscular disease. She said she would contact Dr. Engel's office and arrange a referral.

Both Cheryl and I were devastated. We returned home in shock. We could not talk with each other. Cheryl was in tears. In a few days, Dr. Engel's office called. We made an appointment to see him.

At Dr. Engel's office, we waited in a room with many other patients with neuromuscular diseases. This made me feel hopeful. Like me, these people must think this man offers hope for ending this deadly disease.

After a while, a nurse called me in. Dr. Engel's smile greeted me as he introduced himself. He was a kind and caring man, and he took a long time to examine me. After he finished, he told us that he was not sure that I had ALS. He made an appointment for a special liver test for me. The test required that I stay in a hospital overnight.

The test did not give Dr. Engel the results he was looking for, but he was still not convinced. He ordered a muscle biopsy. The biopsy was taken from my thigh. After getting the results of that test, he was convinced that I had ALS.

Dr. Engel conducted a number of clinical studies with ALS patients and offered me the opportunity to participate in several of them. I was happy to do so. He explained the possible risks involved in participating in each study, but since I already had ALS, I felt I had nothing to lose. Besides, even if the research didn't help me, it might help some other people with ALS. Each new study gave me a new hope. Hope that the treatment would improve my condition. Hope that a cure for ALS would be found.

The Cruel Truth

Cheryl's signed portrait, July 1969

When I received the call from Dr. Hanson, asking me to come to her office the day she made her diagnosis, I knew my worst fears had been true. Ismail had spent months trying to find out the cause of his pain and progressive weakness. I accidentally discovered the terrible truth a couple of days before he did.

I had been writing feature articles for a local newspaper and met a young woman with post-polio syndrome who asked if I would be willing to write an article about her and her support group. A charming, intelligent woman who was adamant about spreading the word about post-polio syndrome and how it impacts the lives of those who have it, she invited me to her home to interview her. She also asked me to attend a meeting of the support group she helped organize and run. The guest speaker at the meeting was a neurologist. When a question came up about ALS, the doctor explained the similarities and differences between post-polio syndrome and ALS. "Some of the symptoms are very similar," she said, "but the prognosis for persons with ALS is very poor. Most people with ALS die within five years of diagnosis."

As she described the symptoms of ALS, I began to panic. They were exactly the same symptoms that Ismail had been having. The fight-or-flight instinct took hold of me. The room closed in. The air strangled. I had to get out of there. I forced myself to remain seated until the lecture was over. It seemed like the longest presentation I ever had to sit through. I didn't hear another word of it.

When the doctor finally finished speaking, I apologized to the planning committee for not being able to stay for the reception they had invited me to. An instant later, I was gasping for air outside in the parking lot.

When I got home, I shut myself up in my office. Listening to the innocent hum of Ismail's lawnmower in the yard, I tore through reference books, trying to learn as much as I could about ALS, praying I'd find something, anything that didn't match Ismail's symptoms. I couldn't. There must be hundreds, maybe thousands of other conditions with the same or similar symptoms, I tried to assure myself. Just because Ismail has those symptoms doesn't mean he has ALS. He can't have ALS. I pictured him outside pushing that lawnmower. Strong. Happy. Optimistic. We have so many plans, so many things we want to do together. Grow our business. Write screenplays. Produce films. He has so much to live for. I couldn't stand to lose him. I won't tell him what I'm thinking. I might be over-reacting. I could be wrong. Oh, God, please let me be wrong.

I couldn't sleep, couldn't eat. Trying to hide my anguish, I put up an optimistic front. On the day of his neurology appointment, I waited for the verdict from Dr. Hanson, praying it would not be the one I expected. The phone rang.

Terrified, I snatched it. It was Ismail. "How was your appointment?" I asked him, forcing myself to sound cheerful.

"Not good." He sounded scared. "They think I have a disease that's spreading in my hand and arm and has started to spread to my tongue."

That fight or flight instinct gripped me again. I wanted so desperately to run away from this.

When Dr. Hanson called she told me she thought Ismail and I both needed to be there when she discussed her diagnosis.

"Is it ALS?" The terrible words tumbled out.

The phone went silent. After what seemed like an eternity, she said "Yes."

"Oh, God!" I began to cry. Dashed in one awful moment were all of the dreams Ismail and I had for a long and happy life together. Early in our relationship, I had given Ismail a photograph and had written in the corner of it "To my darling, with deepest love and affection. I shall always love you as I do today. May we travel through life with a smile and a laugh. Forever yours, Cheryl." Will we ever be able to smile and laugh again? I wondered. Gone were our hopes of building a successful video production company, for writing screenplays and musicals together, for traveling the world. We would never grow old together, like those sweet old couples we often watched strolling hand-in-hand through the park at Santa Monica Beach. I would soon be a widow. I would lose the man I loved so deeply, wanted so desperately. I'd live the rest of my life alone and lonely. And Ismail, so sweet, so cheerful, so full of life, would die young. How could this happen to us?

"How did you know?" Dr. Hanson asked me.

I told her about the meeting I went to, about the neurologist who said ALS patients die within five years.

She sighed her disapproval of the five-year death sentence and tried to reassure me that some people with ALS live longer than that. "It has taken a long time for Ismail's disease to progress to this point," she said. "Hopefully, it will be many more years before he is an invalid."

I flinched at the word "invalid."

"He is going to die, right?" My voice was small and tight with fear.

"We are all going to die," she reminded me. "Each one of us will eventually contract some disease or condition that will prove to be our demise."

I've often remembered that wise response and have been comforted by it. Simple. True. We are all going to die. We begin doing so from the moment we are born. We all hope to live a long life, of course. Some of us are lucky to do so. Some of us are not so lucky. More important than the number of years we live is how we live them. I didn't know how many years I had left with Ismail, but I promised myself that I would make the most of every year, every minute, we had together.

Rescue From My Desert Island

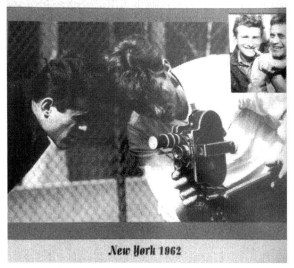

ETERNAL BEST FRIENDS

New York 1962

Ismail and Phil Gries working on a film project at
CCNY in 1962

ALS has taught me who my true friends are. When the disease
eventually took away my ability to speak, I felt like I was left
alone on a desert island with no human or animal life
around me, surrounded by a big ocean without another
piece of land in sight. The silence made it impossible to fight
loneliness. I would force myself to talk so I could hear the
sound of my voice loud and clear. But my situation would not
allow it. I could not talk out loud because my voice had left
me, but I talked to myself in silence.

For one reason or another, most of my friends left me. In
silence I would ask myself why they left. I could not come up
with an answer. Their absence made loneliness and daily life
very difficult to deal with. I was still able to speak for several

more months, even though I had to repeat myself many times to be understood, and I was still able to walk with difficulty. One day I ran into one of my friends and asked him straight out why he did not come to see me. He replied, "I could not handle your situation." With tears in his eyes, he walked away. I never saw him again.

Luckily, all of my relatives and a few good friends have stood by me up to this day. Their support has made life easier to bear. I have two great brothers-in-law and sisters-in-law whom I love very much and who love me. And, I have lots of nieces, grandnieces, nephews, and grandnephews who are beautiful and fun and make me happy.

I am grateful for all of my friends. Phil is like a brother to me. A few years ago he wrote to me:

"Ismail...a brother for life. Our relationship during the past 49 years has been destined by God. We were meant to be in one another's life. Our friendship has been so very special and meaningful to me. You have taught me a lot, and I am wiser, more appreciative and more grateful because of your stead-fastness, strength and courage."

Phil wrote a poem for me and framed it along with a picture of the two of us working together on a film project in college.

Eternal Best Friends
New York 1962

In the fall of '62
A friendship developed, lasting and true
Two young men beginning anew
Motion picture production creating the glue

CCNY halls opened wide
For exploration side by side
Till Hollywood beckoned its call
Living together and searching for all.

Beverly Hills studio apartment
Tiny and cramped
With barely a place for a functioning lamp
Paying $55.00 monthly apiece
And just getting by on a one-year lease

One working at AV-ED Films by day
The other studying cinema at UCLA
Evenings at home
Returning to compare
Our thoughts, our dreams
One common prayer.

Jane and Cheryl entered our lives
Eventually becoming our beautiful wives.
Continuous days and nights askew
Memories of everything and nothing to do.

Phil's professional frustration
A pivotal thrust
Leaving L.A.
And kicking the dust.

Our geography changed
Our greetings were short
Communicating now
From a New York port.

A passion for film
Kept us abreast.
Our distance kept me
From knowing the rest.

Then our reunion in '89.
That unforgettable embrace

With hardly any movement
Only a trace.

Profound new chapters.
Some call it strife.
With major challenges
For you and your wife.

Your health compromised,
Your journey astray.
Reflections of life's changes
In God's mysterious way.

Thoroughly scrutinized
In all medical logs
More than a dozen years elapsed
Defying the odds.

A supreme power to influence
With such great will
Your inspiration to others
All sharing the same pill.

A reflection of courage
Represents your stand
From far off Albania
To this promised land.

An overwhelming desire
To always be you
With fierce determination
Not to be blue.

Though few really know
What you have been through

There is one special person
As remarkable as you.

Cheryl your wife
Love of your life
With a heart so true
Devoted to you

An inspiration to all
An eternal best friend
Admiration for you
Will never ever end.

So with sentiment I conclude
May you always prevail
You are like a brother to me.
I love you, Ismail

May God bless Phil and all of my other friends and relatives who have loved and helped me through the years. The most important person in my life, who plays the most difficult role, is my wife. With Cheryl's undying love, she became my best friend who helps keep my dreams and hopes alive. Day by day, she helps me with daily quality of life, living life at its best.

Inspiration and Hope

Ismail with Stephen Hawking in Beverly Hills, CA, August 14, 1992

After learning Ismail's diagnosis, I became depressed and afraid and slipped into intense mourning. It weighed on me so heavily I felt I couldn't move. It seemed to take hours for me to walk from my car to the entrance of the supermarket. Then I heard the story of Stephen Hawking's life.

Astrophysicist Stephen Hawking, one of the greatest minds of all time, has survived ALS for more than 50 years. He has been an inspiration to many people who battle incurable, life-threatening illnesses. According to the biography on his official website (**http://www.hawking.org.uk /index.html**): "In spite of being wheelchair bound and dependent on a computerised voice system for communication, Stephen Hawking continues to combine family life (he has three children and three grandchildren) and his research into theoretical physics together with an extensive programme of travel and public lectures. He still hopes to make it into space one day."

Professor Hawking's remarkable story touched me profoundly and helped lead me out of the darkness of my depression and back into the brightness of hope. If this world-renowned scientist, I thought, can continue to work and travel and accomplish great things despite being in a wheelchair and dependent on a computer voice system for communication, so can Ismail. I resolved to help Ismail live his life to the fullest for as long as he could.

During the course of Ismail's disease, he has produced videos, written a screenplay, co-written two musicals with me, and conceived, co-developed, and co-founded a social network, Honest Course (**http://www.honestcourse.com**), which celebrates honesty and integrity in society, government, and individuals' lives. He has written blogs for Honest Course by spelling out sentences to me by blinking his eye, one letter at a time. He wrote chapters for this book the same way.

Meeting Our Hero

Ismail and I met Stephen Hawking on August 14, 1992. It was one of the most exciting nights of our lives. We were guests of the ALS Association at the world premiere of a new movie about his life and work, *A Brief History of Time*, and were invited to a private reception for Professor Hawking at the Peninsula Hotel in Beverly Hills prior to the screening. Meeting Shirley MacLaine and Sidney Poitier that night was exciting, but meeting the brilliant theoretical physicist was the thrill of a lifetime. Our hero and inspiration was right there in front of us!

He and his gracious companion were introduced to us. He spoke! He said something to us! But what? The noise of the room drowned out the words of his electronic voice synthesizer. The moment of a lifetime, and I couldn't hear his words!

"Did you hear what he said?" his companion asked.

"No," I admitted meekly, hoping it was something profound.

"He said 'It is a pleasure to meet you.'"

"It is a great honor to meet you," I told him. And, in a moment, he was gone, moving on to greet other guests.

Later that evening, we watched his limousine arrive at the theatre, watched attendants bring him out. Stephen Hawking, perhaps the man with the most brilliant mind in the world, was arriving for the premiere of his movie, and we were there with him!

An usher directed us to an area inside the theatre that had been reserved for people in wheelchairs. "You will not be able to stay with him," he informed me and the nurse who was with us. There's no room in this area. You'll have to sit over there." He pointed to the other side of the auditorium.

"No, we have to stay with him, in case there is a problem with his ventilator," I explained.

"It's against fire code. He'll be fine."

"At least one of us has to stay with him," I insisted.

"I'm sorry. You can't. He'll be fine."

I asked to speak with the manager, to see whether I could reason with him and negotiate an exception.

The usher went to speak to the manager for me. But he came back with bad news. No dice. "The fire department won't allow it." He assured us we would be close enough to hear Ismail's ventilator, that we could easily reach him if there was any problem.

Ismail, as usual trying to be the tough guy, assured us he would be okay. So, the nurse and I reluctantly left him and went to our seats. We glanced at him frequently across the room to make sure he was all right. Then, the lights went out. Several moments of silent darkness. Stephen Hawking's electronic voice pierced the silence. "Let's go!"

The audience erupted into laughter, and the film started. A couple of minutes later the awful beeping of Ismail's ventilator filled the theatre. "Oh, God!" I thought. "I knew this was going to happen!"

The nurse and I bolted from our seats. I crawled over the laps of the people sitting between Ismail and me, smashing feet and tripping over legs—"Excuse me! Excuse me! I'm sorry!" Once through the tangles of legs and feet, I dove into a sea of wheelchairs. Where was he? It was so dark. I tripped over wheels and leg rests, following the sound of the beeps. "Excuse me! Excuse me! Sorry! So sorry!"

Our nurse reached Ismail before I did. She had run out the back door of the auditorium and across the lobby, back into the auditorium on the other side where Ismail was. His ventilator circuit (the tubing that connected him to the ventilator) had become disconnected, and he was getting no air. The nurse quickly found the problem even in the dark and reconnected the circuit. The beeping stopped, and Ismail was fine again. The nurse and I stood glued to the side of Ismail's wheelchair for the remainder of the movie. No one made us move.

Thank God Ismail was all right. On the way out, I shot the usher an "I told you!" glare.

Sitting on a shelf in our home is the framed snapshot that begins this chapter of Stephen Hawking and Ismail, sitting side-by-side in their wheelchairs at the Peninsula Hotel reception. Ismail and I both treasure the picture and the memory of meeting this amazing man.

What ALS Will Never Take From Me

Ismail and his buddy Charlie at a Walk to Defeat ALS event,
October 2009

ALS has robbed me of my ability to move my body, but it will never take away my feelings or my dreams. Most important, it will never steal my thinking process or my intelligence.

All my life I have been hungry for knowledge. I keep informed by watching local and world news every night. One of the ways I continue to exercise my mind is by watching game shows such as *Jeopardy* and *Wheel of Fortune*. I play the games in my mind as I watch them. Sometimes Cheryl pauses the television and asks me if I know the answer to a final Jeopardy question. If I say "yes," she has me spell out the answer with eye blinks. Most of the time, I get the answer right. Cheryl and my nurses are surprised at how much I know and remember. It is because I am thinking all the time. Since I can't move my body, all of my activity is in my mind.

I promised myself, and Cheryl agreed, that I would not spend the rest of my life lying in bed. Cheryl and I like to go places. Because I have an active mind and always will, I can remember all the many places I have travelled in my life. I can revisit them again and again in my mind. I can imagine new and exciting places to visit, and I can come back to them whenever I want.

My biggest dream is to keep writing books and musicals with Cheryl. I dream that one day one of the musicals Cheryl and I write together will get produced on Broadway. Cheryl and I will continue dreaming as long as we live. ALS will never take that away from me.

The Fighter with the Winning Smile

Ismail in Solvang, CA.

Ismail has always been a fighter. He has battled ALS as he has every other challenge in his life—tirelessly, determined to win. Some of the most painful moments for me these past 30 years have been those in which I've watched him struggle to do things he could no longer do. My heart ached as he continued fighting to walk long after his legs had grown weak and he was unsteady on his feet. I fought back tears as he tried over and over to take my photograph when his arms were too weak to hold up the camera. Each weekend he struggled, exhausted, to push his lawnmower around his meticulously groomed yard, then disassemble the mower and clean each part, fumbling with the cleaned pieces until he was able to put them back together. It hurt me when he insisted on helping wash the dishes and dropped them because his hands could no longer hold a plate. "Damn hands!" he cursed, glaring at them, his face screwed up into a grimace of frustration.

Because he has lost control of most of the muscles of his body and is forced to depend on other people to clean him, feed him, move him, and keep him alive, it has become more and more important to him to control those things he still can. As strong-minded and strong-willed as ever, he remains in complete control of his health care, his diet, and his daily routine. He selects the clothes he wants to wear, the food he wants to eat, the television programs he wants to watch, when and how long he wants to sunbathe on our backyard patio, and the times of his appointments with home health nurses, respiratory therapists, medical equipment technicians, and visits from friends and family. Everyone rearranges their schedules to accommodate his. They don't mind because everyone loves Ismail.

He also has the final say in family money matters. We go together to meet with our financial advisor, and he participates in all financial decisions. I don't dare make any large purchases without first getting Ismail's approval. He even has veto power over smaller purchases. I sometimes have to sneak shopping bags into the house without him seeing them until I find the right time to show him my amazing bargains! Sometimes, when my powers of persuasion fail, I have to return those bargains to the store for a refund. It's only right. We are a team, and it's his money too. Of course, we have the same kind of money squabbles as other married couples (sometimes I want to keep that great bargain I just bought or really, really want to buy a new television set). It's worked out well over the last 44 years, though. I love to spend money, and Ismail's insistent "No!" has often kept my spending in line.

If you don't believe that Ismail, totally paralyzed and unable to speak, could have the persuasive power to get his way, you have never heard him grind his teeth! And he doesn't stop until he gets his way! He has always had a streak of stubbornness. As his wife, I have often found that streak frustrating, even infuriating. At the same time, I'm grateful he has it because that stubbornness has driven him to fight to stay alive and productive for so many years.

Ismail has two lethal weapons that have helped him conquer many problems and survive even the darkest of times. One is his great sense of humor, which he has never lost, despite the struggle, the pain, and the loss he has endured throughout the years. He laughs a lot and enjoys a good joke. He frequently tells his own jokes, usually laughing so hard as he's telling one that he has trouble blinking out the punch line. By the time he gets to it, we're all laughing with him so much that the punch line is anticlimactic.

He avoids watching depressing movies, but enjoys comedies, both current movies and classics. He has many favorites. He especially loves *Singing in the Rain; Don't Go Near the Water; Analyze This*, and *One, Two, Three*. We have a tradition of watching *Young Frankenstein* every Halloween and officially launch the holiday season each year by watching the Albert Finney musical version of *Scrooge*. Ismail also loves some of the reruns of classic television comedies, such as *Dick Van Dyke, Mary Tyler Moore, Hogan's Heroes*, and *The Honeymooners*. I can sometimes hear him laughing all the way in the other room when he's enjoying a good comedy. He makes a distinctive sound when he laughs, and I know when he's having a good time.

Ismail's second lethal weapon is his beautiful smile. One of the things I am most grateful for is that although ALS has robbed Ismail of control of most of his voluntary muscles and left him unable to move his arms, hands, legs, feet, and head, it has not stolen his smile. I will continue to encourage and enjoy every smile I can as long as ALS allows.

Ismail's smile has melted many a heart. People often walk up to us in restaurants, in shops, and on the street and tell us how we have inspired them. Many years ago we were at a

Sunday brunch at a local Mexican restaurant. Ismail was still able to eat food by mouth at that time, but I had to feed him each bite because he was unable to use his hands and arms. We were both enjoying the delicious food when a couple stopped at our table on their way out of the restaurant. "I just want to tell you what an inspiration you are," the man told us. "We have been watching the two of you, and the love you have for one another is touching."

Another time, we were window-shopping in Carmel. We had attended a Bach chamber concert the night before, and I had felt self-conscious because the sound of Ismail's ventilator could be heard over the quiet music in the small room. We weren't in a place where we could easily leave without disrupting the concert, and I worried that the noise of the ventilator was diminishing the enjoyment of the concert for the other attendees. A couple approached us on the street. "Hello," the man said. "We saw you at the concert last night." I braced myself. Here it comes. He's going to complain that the noise we made ruined the concert. I tried to quickly formulate an apology. "We were so glad to see you there," the man told Ismail. "It's wonderful that you were able to attend the concert and enjoy the music." What a nice man! What a generous couple! I let out a deep breath of relief and thanked him, wishing him and his wife a good day. Ismail flashed them his disarming smile.

Everyone at the medical clinic knows Ismail. And at the medical center. And at the dentist's office. The nurses and receptionists ask about him every time I go in for my own appointments. I'm known as Ismail's wife wherever I go. When we take him in for his appointments, he charms everybody with that big, gorgeous smile of his. The radiologist spends extra time with him, keeping him comfortable and making sure she gets a good x-ray even though she has to take the film with him sitting in his wheelchair instead of lying on the table. He always gives her a smile and spells out "Thank you." One young, attractive phlebotomist told him she loved the "color of his blood."

There's a pick-up line for you!   Don't think he didn't enjoy it! Always the ladies' man, he loves the attention he gets from women.   And yes, I frequently catch his eyes following a pretty woman passing by!

So Ismail goes on smiling and laughing and charming his way through every day, every year. He says, "To die is easy; to live is a challenge."   He has always been ready for that challenge. I know he'll continue to fight.

A Few of My Favorite Things

Ismail and Cheryl in front of mural inside Gene Autry's
National Center, August 2006.

I was once asked to share some things about myself that most people don't know. Coming up with that list made me think about all the things I love the most in the world. I will talk about some of those here, and you can read a longer list of my favorite things in the Appendix.

Of course my wife, Cheryl, is at the top of the list. She is my best friend, and we share a mutual respect. She is very thoughtful and easy to talk to. It is easy to discuss difficult problems with her. Together we fight every battle and have fun too!

Almost everyone who knows me can tell you I love Westerns and watch them all the time. People ask me why I love western movies so much. It is because they are like fairy tales. They tell the story of pioneers and explorers, of good and evil, and of heroes of the American past.

People are often surprised to find out that even though I can no longer eat by mouth, I love watching the Food Channel. People ask me why. It's because food keeps us alive and feeds our souls. My favorite show is Guy Fieri's *Diners, Drive-Ins, and Dives* because it shows different places to eat throughout our great country and different types of ethnic food.

Elephants are my favorite animal. They are majestic and fun to watch. I also love tropical birds and see the bird show every time I go to the Los Angeles Zoo. With their colorful feathers, they are beautiful and are easy to train for shows. Some of them make wonderful pets. I like giraffes a lot, too. With their heads up high in the air, they seem to me to be the proudest of all animals in the animal kingdom.

My favorite color is yellow because it is bright and cheerful, and it stands up over the other colors. Yet it soothes and is very appealing to my eyes and my soul.

I like opera because it tells stories in harmony and beautiful music. I love the arias, the costumes, the singing, and the sets.

I enjoy many kinds of music. Franz Schubert is my favorite classical composer, but I also love the music of Johann Sebastian Bach and Ludwig Van Beethoven. I enjoy songs from musical comedies, too. My favorite musical is *Singing in the Rain*. I like listening to many popular singers of yesterday to today, from Perry Como to Beyonce.

I love world literature. In fact, Cheryl and I co-wrote the book for a musical about Edgar Allan Poe. The title is *Call Me Eddy*, and it is about a fictitious meeting of Emily Dickinson and Edgar Allan Poe. We once had a staged reading of this musical at the Stella Adler Theatre in Hollywood. A couple of years ago, we had another staged reading of some of the scenes at the La Canada Theatre.

I have traveled to a lot of countries. After the United States, my second favorite country is Italy because of its history, culture, art, and music. I especially love beautiful Venice with its canals and gondolas. It is one of the most romantic cities in the world.

There are many things in this world of ours to see and do. But most of all, I want to be with my wife as long as God allows. I enjoy my family and their kids. Seeing the children growing up is a pleasure.

Death is an end of all things on earth. Life is a celebration. I want to enjoy the part of the world that belongs to me and celebrate life.

Exploring the World Together

Ismail and Cheryl in St. Mark's Square, Venice, Italy, October 1989

Ismail had done a lot of traveling before I met him. With the exception of living and working in London for three months at the age of 18 with my best friend, Sherry D'Attile, I had not. I yearned to travel. I wanted to see the world with Ismail, hoping that he would show me all the places he had seen, that we would explore lots of new places together.

Early in our marriage, before the expenses and responsibilities of owning a home tied us down, we took a Caribbean cruise. It was relaxing on the ship, fun touring the islands, but also sad witnessing the poverty of third world countries. We were young then, just beginning our marriage. This would be the first of many travels, we thought.

Making the most of our trip, we planned a stopover in New Orleans on the return home and scheduled it so we would be there during Mardi Gras. Everyone should experience Mardi Gras — at least once in their lives! Wall-to-wall people in the French Quarter where we stayed. People sleeping on sidewalks. On Mardi Gras Day, we stood still in the middle of Bourbon Street and let the movement of the crowd carry us down the street like a swelling ocean wave bringing us onto shore. The streets were full of flashy costumes. Skimpy costumes. Some very skimpy! Elaborate floats in noisy parades. The sky was filled with flying beads and trinkets. Crowds surged to grab the beads while pickpockets worked them. It was the only time in my life I had my wallet stolen.

Racing Through Europe

In 1989, when Ismail was in an early stage of ALS, while he was still able to walk and before he started using a ventilator to breathe, we went on a 14-day escorted European tour. We wanted to see as much of the world together as we could, while we could. We visited seven countries in those 14 days: England, Holland, West Germany, Austria, Italy, Switzerland, and France. Two days per country.

We had a lot of fun, but it was hard work too. Although Ismail was still able to walk on his own, getting around was beginning to become more difficult for him, and at times he was unsteady on his feet. He could no longer carry luggage, although he tried. This was before wheeled luggage became the norm, and ours had none. It was painful for me to watch him struggling heroically with those heavy bags. So I carried the luggage, with the help of some compassionate tour mates. Throughout the tour, Ismail and I moved more slowly than the others in our group and faced each flight of stairs as a daunting challenge. Yet we were determined to see everything — and we did, one laborious step and stair at a time.

There was so much we wanted to do in London, but we had time only for a quick bus tour of the city and a visit to Westminster Abbey. Ismail wanted to tour the Tower of London. It was his only London request. But by the time we got there, the Tower was closed for the day. I was more heartbroken than he was. Ismail would probably never get to London again, would never have another chance to see the inside of the Tower.

We saw Amsterdam with its intricate network of canals, charming 17th century houses, and bridges.

We marveled at the gothic steeples of the Dom Cathedral in Cologne. We had lunch at a McDonald's in that city (yes, McDonald's — not our first choice for regional cuisine, but we were short on time that day and good old McDonald's was nearby). Ismail was participating in a clinical study at the time that required him to mix a spoonful of a clinical trial medication, a white powder, into his food. Other customers stared with suspicion as we pulled out an unmarked plastic bag of white powder and stirred some of it into Ismail's food. Ismail mugged exaggerated expressions of disgust as he ate, trying to convince onlookers that the powder was not some sort of illegal drug. He must have been convincing because we weren't arrested. Fortunately, Dr. Engel, who was conducting the clinical trial, gave us a letter to carry with us throughout Europe, testifying that he prescribed that medication as part of a research project. The letter sure came in handy when we were going through customs on our way back into the United States. The customs officer read the letter, looked us over carefully, and must have decided Ismail had an honest face. He let us back into the country, white powder and all.

We took a cruise down the Rhine. Castles, like fairytale visions, gleamed on top of steep cliffs along the banks.

We marveled at the panoramic view from the peak of Mt. Pilatus in Switzerland and walked around the medieval town of Lucerne. We bought a beautiful Swiss cuckoo clock with little wooden dancers that twirl around to charming tinkling music every hour. "That cuckoo clock won't last very long," a member of our tour group warned us. "Cuckoo clocks stop working after a short time." But with a few periodic minor repairs, ours continues to work even today, 25 years later. It has charmed many children, including our nieces and nephews and, now that they have children of their own, our grandnieces and grand-nephews too. Like Ismail, this memento of our European travels has survived beyond people's predictions.

After a good night's sleep, I was ready to see Paris. We saw many famous landmarks, including a tour inside Notre Dame, the Louvre, and a cruise on the Seine River.

If I had to choose a favorite city on our tour, it would be Venice, the romantic city floating on the sea. At St. Mark's Square, with its elaborate Basilica and swarm of friendly pigeons, I took a great snapshot of Ismail with a pigeon perched on his shoulder.

We took a moonlight gondola ride with a serenading gondolier. Since Ismail was unsteady on his feet, men helped him into the gondola after everyone else had boarded. At the end of the ride, they assisted him back out. I watched nervously from the pier as they pulled him out of the boat, worried that he would lose his footing and fall into the water. As the men brought him up onto the pier, I took a step backward to get out of their way. My foot went over the edge of the pier, and I lost my own balance. I fell backward, plunging into the Grand Canal! I was humiliated—and scared. I can't swim. I clutched one of the pilings for dear life while the pier slammed into my fingers with every ripple of the water, breaking one of them I learned a couple of weeks later when I finally went to a doctor. The poor gondoliers had to quickly get Ismail on sure footing and then rush over to fish me out of the water! I returned to the hotel dripping wet, my hair, my new coat, my shoes, my handbag and everything inside my bag soaked. The hotel clerks laughed at me. "Did you enjoy your swim in the canal?" one of them smirked. I wouldn't tell anyone the story for years. I swore Ismail to secrecy!

On our way home from Europe, we stopped in New York to visit our friends, Phil and Jane. It was mid-October, and the fall colors were vibrant. Phil took us out to collect a few crimson leaves and into Manhattan for a visit to Times Square and a special dinner. We saw *Les Miserables* on Broadway. This short but quality time with good friends was the perfect ending to our travels.

I Chose to Live

Ismail enjoying the Huntington Library and Botanical Gardens

Eventually my ALS progressed to the point that it made it difficult for me to breathe. I would keep my mouth open in front of a fan so I would feel like I was breathing easily, or I would put my head outside of a car window or my face straight toward an air conditioner. I would wake up at night in pain, struggling to breathe. I would ask myself "Why me?" The answer was always the same. "My luck."

There is an old saying: "When God closes a door, He opens a window." I had married the most wonderful woman in the world. She has become a great friend and supporter, as well as a great wife, and she is loyal to our mutual love.

One day in 1990, we were on our way home from our video production company to pack to go to Las Vegas the next day. We were planning to renew our marriage vows on our twenty-year wedding anniversary. Suddenly, a coughing spell and shortness of breath overcame me. The cough would not stop, and breathing became more and more difficult. Cheryl turned the car around and took me to an emergency room. By the time they examined me, the coughing and shortness of breath had stopped. Unable to find anything wrong with me, the doctor sent me home. He told me to return if my symptoms came back. Cheryl had to decide whether to cancel our trip. I told her I would be okay.

The next morning, I woke up coughing again and struggling to get my breath. Instead of going to Las Vegas, we met my pulmonologist, a wonderful and supportive doctor named Dr. Edward Anthony Oppenheimer, at another emergency room. After examining me, Dr. Oppenheimer told Cheryl and me that we had to make a decision. We had talked before about whether we wanted to use a ventilator when I was no longer able to breathe on my own. Cheryl and I had decided we wanted to do that. Dr. Oppenheimer explained that I could wait a little longer, but if I did, my condition would probably get worse, and I might have a bigger emergency. That would make the situation more dangerous.

We decided that it was time for me to go on a ventilator. Instead of renewing our vows and celebrating our anniversary in Las Vegas, Cheryl and I spent Thanksgiving weekend in the hospital, waiting for my surgery that had been scheduled for Monday morning, November 26, the day of our anniversary.

That weekend was one of the longest ones of my life. Cheryl and I had a lot of time to think and worry. Were we making the right decision by having the surgery now? We had several discussions with Dr. Oppenheimer about things to expect and think about, but now that we had made our decision, we started to have second thoughts. There was a chance I wouldn't be able to talk after the surgery. Would I still be able to eat? Should I wait, I wondered, until I had to have the surgery to save my life?

Cheryl and I made a list of all of our questions and called Dr. Engel, the neuromuscular disease specialist. He had given us a phone number where we could reach him after hours. We felt bad calling him during the Thanksgiving weekend when he was at home with his family, and we weren't sure he would be able to call us back, but he did. Dr. Engel talked to us for a long time and reassured us that he didn't mind that we called. He told us he could not give us advice about whether to use a ventilator because that was a very personal decision that we had to make for ourselves, but he answered all of our questions the best he could and gave us lots of encouragement. We felt a lot better after talking with him.

Later, however, as I was lying in my hospital bed in the quiet hospital room with Cheryl stretched out asleep in a big chair next to me, my mind started wandering. My first question was "Is Cheryl going to accept me with the ventilator?" Even though she was sure we had made the right decision, I worried she might change her mind. I asked myself how the rest of our family and our friends would react. Would they think of me differently now? What about my clients? Would they leave me and find another video production company to work with? Dear God, help me make the right decision. I reassured myself that Cheryl will always love me and that my family and friends will be there for me. My clients know me and my work, I told myself. They won't leave me and my production company just because I use a ventilator. Convincing myself that everything would be all right, I chose to live.

The surgery went fine. When I was back in my hospital room, Cheryl brought hors d'oeuvres and sparkling apple cider for the nurses to help us celebrate the success of my surgery and our twenty years of marriage. Happy anniversary to us! This was the beginning of a new life.

Everything's Under Control—NOT!

Cheryl and Ismail 2003

I was in the hospital with Ismail day and night following his tracheotomy. I got little sleep, and each new day brought additional fatigue and stress, but I refused to leave Ismail's side. Dr. Hanson stopped in to see him once a day. Every time she came, she looked at me with deep concern. "You'd better get as much rest as you can now," she warned. "Once Ismail comes home, it's going to be challenging for you."

"Okay," I'd tell her, but I wouldn't leave his hospital room. How could I? He needed me there more than ever. And I wanted to be there, to talk to all the doctors who stopped in, to make sure he was getting everything he needed, to be his advocate. Besides, I wondered, what could be so hard about taking care of him on a ventilator? So I'll have to clean ventilator equipment once a day and set up the next day's circuitry. I'll have to suction him through his tracheostomy tube a few times a day. Big deal. I couldn't think of anything that would make my life harder or more stressful than it was already. I'm strong. I'm competent. I can handle anything. Everything is under control.

Dr. Oppenheimer planned to have Ismail breathe on his own without the assistance of the ventilator during the day and use the ventilator for eight hours only while he slept at night.

The hospital staff had been tasked with weaning him off the ventilator during the day, but Ismail couldn't tolerate breathing on his own for long periods of time. After a few minutes, he became short of breath and began begging for the ventilator. He grew more and more distressed until the hospital staff relented and put him back on it. This made Dr. Oppenheimer unhappy because he believed that, with patience, Ismail could grow more comfortable breathing on his own. After all, he wasn't using a ventilator when he walked into the hospital only a few days before! "Think about how he was before he had the tracheotomy," Dr. Oppenheimer suggested.

Before the tracheotomy? I remembered watching Ismail grow more and more tired, sick-looking, weak. Once a workhorse, he became unable to complete a full day's work. I bought a twin bed and set it up in a back room of his office so he could lie down and take a nap in the middle of the day. Unheard of! I realized now that he had been in respiratory failure for months, and it had been growing increasingly worse.

When I explained to Dr. Oppenheimer how tired and weak he was before coming into the hospital, the doctor told me that hopefully overnight ventilation would give Ismail the strength and energy he needed to get through each day breathing on his own. So the weaning process continued, painful, unsuccessful. When Ismail was discharged from the hospital, the responsibility of weaning him off the ventilator was transferred to me.

So we came home. It was just Ismail and me—and this new intimidating machine that kept him alive. Before discharge, I promised Dr. Oppenheimer that I'd keep Ismail off the ventilator for increasingly longer periods of time during the day until he became comfortable using the ventilator only in bed at night.

Yeah, right. Ismail immediately went into respiratory distress as soon as I turned off the ventilator, screwing up his face into a tortured grimace, sweating profusely. He would beg for the ventilator. I would beg him to try to relax and breathe on his own. He would beg more desperately for the ventilator. My emotions were torn to shreds. I was torturing the man I loved, but it was necessary for his own good. Emotionally broken, torn with anger and guilt, I would finally turn on the ventilator and give Ismail the air for which he begged. Soon he would calm down and become comfortable again. I would feel like a total failure.

The hospital's social worker had given me a list of caregivers I could call to find someone to hire to care for Ismail during the day while I was at work. I had used up all of my vacation time staying with Ismail in the hospital, so I had to get back to my job right away. I began calling the people on the list. Most of the numbers were no longer in service. I left messages at the few numbers that were still active. No one called back.

I'll just hire a caregiver from an agency, I decided, until I can find someone to hire independently. I looked up caregiver agencies in the phone book and called to inquire about non-licensed aides. As soon as I mentioned "ventilator" the agencies cut me off. They didn't provide aides for people on ventilators. Agencies are required to provide licensed vocational nurses (LVNs) or registered nurses (RNs) to care for ventilator patients. And licensed nurses, especially those provided by agencies, are expensive. Very expensive. An agency-provided LVN's hourly rate exceeded my own salary.

I'd be losing money by going back to work! I called adult day care centers. They refused to take someone on a ventilator. Did I know any family members or friends who could participate in Ismail's care? No. Everyone had their own families, jobs, responsibilities. I could count on them for short-term help in emergencies, but not for ongoing, long-term commitments. Could I quit my job and stay home to care for Ismail 24/7? Not if Ismail and I wanted to keep our house and continue to pay our bills. To complicate matters, Ismail's medical insurance was provided as part of my employee benefits. I had to keep my job so we could continue his health care. I seemed to be stuck in an impossible situation. I began to feel frightened. Trapped. No way out. I struggled to push away the negative thoughts. I'm in control. I can do this. Other families do this. How?

I had trouble keeping up with the cleaning and setting up of ventilator equipment. I was constantly interrupted by visiting home health nurses, respiratory therapists, supply deliveries, and Ismail needing my assistance. I found myself tangled up in ventilator circuits, unsure of what to connect to what, frantically poring over instructions and diagrams. Dirty circuits and tubing piled up, needing to be disinfected and hung to dry. The home health nurse complained that the equipment wasn't cleaned and set up when she came to visit, insisting that it was critical to have the back-up ventilator ready to go at all times in case a problem arose with the ventilator Ismail was on. I can do that. Everything's under control.

As time went on, I felt more and more overwhelmed. Oh, so this is what Dr. Hanson was talking about. This is not as easy as I thought it would be!

I didn't want Dr. Oppenheimer to know how overwhelmed I felt. If he thought I couldn't handle caring for Ismail at home, he might recommend that he be placed in a skilled nursing facility. I couldn't let that happen. Never! I'll get it together. Eventually. In the meantime, whenever Dr. Oppenheimer called I put on my cheeriest voice. Sitting there on the verge of a nervous breakdown, in the midst of dirty ventilator tubing, unmade beds, piles of unwashed dishes, overflowing baskets of laundry, and Ismail desperately begging me to put him back on the ventilator, I told the doctor that everything was going fine. No, I hadn't yet been able to wean Ismail off the ventilator, but I was working on it. Still working on it. Everything else was just fine.

The registered nurse from Home Health checked in on us frequently, often showing up at times of turmoil. She kept encouraging me to tell Dr. Oppenheimer that I was having trouble handling things. "I'm okay," I lied to her.

Eventually, the nurse told him herself. Dr. Oppenheimer arranged for Ismail to be readmitted to the hospital for reassessment, to find out why he couldn't be weaned off the ventilator. I felt humiliated. I was angry at the home health nurse for blowing my cover. I soon realized that her confiding in the doctor was the best thing that could have happened.

We were soon back in the hospital for several more days. When the hospital staff was again unable to wean Ismail off the ventilator during the day, Dr. Oppenheimer rewrote his orders to 24-hour-a-day ventilator care. This made Ismail eligible to participate in a special home ventilator pilot program that provided a primary and a back-up ventilator, additional equipment and supplies, and some skilled nursing care that gave me the help I so desperately needed and enabled me to go back to my job.

Since then the home ventilator pilot program has ended, and the policy has changed. However, families that had participated in the pilot program were grandfathered in and allowed to continue to receive benefits that had been provided under the program, including private duty home nursing care. I was able to continue to work full-time, knowing that my husband was comfortable, safe, and well cared for.

Let Me "Talk"

Spelling Chart

1. a   b   c   d
2. e   f   g   h
3. i   j   k   l
4. m   n   o   p   q
5. r   s   t   u
6. v   w   x   y   z
7. end of word
8. 1234567890
one blink = yes
two blinks = no

Ismail's Spelling Chart

When I first went on the ventilator, a special device called a Passy-Muir valve that I still wear attached to my trach tube (the tube inserted into my tracheostomy) allowed me to continue to talk. Eventually, however, ALS left me totally paralyzed and silent. I told myself that nothing good would ever happen to me again.

Then it happened—hope of hope—the possibility of communication appeared! With the help of a dedicated and great nurse, we created a spelling chart. Cheryl or a nurse calls out the numbers of each row. I blink when I hear the number of the row I want. I blink again when I hear the letter

I need. Letter by letter, I spell out words. Words build into sentences. With these words and sentences I can express my feelings, dreams, hopes, and daily needs. I know it is a difficult and slow process, but with determination and lots of patience my caregivers and I overcome these difficulties.

It's easy to use my spelling chart, but communicating with it takes a special skill. It can be frustrating with new nurses who have not perfected using the chart. Sometimes they think they have memorized it but then forget the letters in the rows, and I have to remind them to look at the chart.

The person I am spelling with has to call out the numbers and letters in a steady rhythm—not too fast, not too slow. If they don't continue to follow the rhythm we have established, we will go "out of sync" with one another, and I will have trouble blinking at the right time. For example, if the person calls out letters and numbers too fast, by the time I blink for the first row, he or she may think I'm blinking for the third or fourth row. If the person calls out letters too slowly, I may blink too soon, and the speller will become confused. We'll have to keep trying to spell over and over until my rhythm and theirs comes into sync.

It is very frustrating when people try to guess a word before they give me a chance to spell it out. If they guess the wrong word, I have to blink twice for "no" and then start spelling the word over again. Sometimes we'll have to spell over and over until the person guesses right or I complete the spelling of the word. This is not only a waste of time but also a lot of extra blinks can become tiring for me.

It's also frustrating and tiring when the speller forgets the letters that I have already selected, and we have to keep spelling the same words over and over. It's helpful for people to write down the words while we're spelling, especially when I have a lot to say.

I'm not able to participate as much as I would like in group conversations. Sometimes, when I'm listening to people talk, there is a lot I'd like to say but I can't jump in and say it. I have to get the attention of Cheryl or my nurse to help me spell out what I want to say one letter at a time. This means the group has to stop and wait for me to spell, and this can sometimes take a long time. Even if I want to say a lot about something, I have to limit the number of words I spell to short sentences or phrases. This means I have to be very succinct. I guess it's good to be succinct, but sometimes there is much more I would have said if I still had my voice. It's especially hard for me to spell out punch lines to jokes. By the time I finish spelling, the punch line has lost its punch!

A computer could not help me in these situations because by the time I could type out what I wanted to say and make the voice synthesizer read it, the group would be on a totally different topic! Even pre-programmed phrases take time to locate and select on a computer.

Although my ability to "talk" is limited and communication can sometimes be frustrating, I'm grateful I can still communicate with members of my family, my caregivers, and anyone else who is willing to learn the system. Blink by blink, letter by letter, word by word, sentence by sentence I express myself.

The Miracle of Communication

Ismail practicing with an eye gaze system

The greatest fear for people living with ALS is that there will come a day when they become "locked in" — so completely paralyzed in the late stages of the disease that even the simplest of muscle movements have been stolen from them. They are unable to communicate in any way with the outside world. Those who are "locked in" survive in complete isolation. They can see and hear everything around them, comprehend everything, think complex thoughts, experience joy, sorrow, and pain, and yearn to communicate with their loved ones and caregivers, to express their feelings, their discomfort, and their desires, but they are hopelessly trapped inside their bodies with no way of communicating with anyone.

For Ismail and me, as well as for others with ALS and their families, overcoming communication barriers and fighting off the "locked in" syndrome is a lifelong battle. And an absolutely essential one. After all, Ismail loves to talk, and he has a lot to say. He's not going to let ALS or anything else shut him up!

Fortunately, there are many tools and products that can help people overcome communication obstacles, and we have used several of them throughout the years. The simplest and cheapest of the tools we have used and continue to use is Ismail's spelling chart. It may be low tech, but it sure does get the job done! Since Ismail and his caregivers all memorize the chart, there's no reason to carry it around—it's all in our heads! It's simple to learn and allows Ismail to say whatever he wants—compliments, complaints, jokes and all!

It's always amusing to watch people's reactions when we're out in public spelling with Ismail. The nurse and I will be standing in front of him, calling out numbers and letters and watching Ismail's series of blinks, slowly building words and sentences that way, while others stare in amazement, thinking we're using some complex code. Inevitably they ask "How do you do that?"

I take Ismail with me whenever I need a tough negotiator for a new car or other big purchase. He's a much better negotiator than I am. I succumb to emotional reactions (What a cute car! What a beautiful color! It's got a back-up camera!). Ismail never does. Of course, this is often frustrating for me when I want Ismail's approval as much as the salesperson does and Ismail makes a demand I don't believe the dealer will ever agree to. That's why my husband is an effective negotiator and, left on my own, I'm often a pushover.

I love watching automobile salespeople, who don't take Ismail seriously at first, have to wait while Ismail blinks out his questions and objections, demanding lower prices and better financing. I explain that Ismail is the one who has to make the decision and that we can't seal the deal until he gives us his one-blink approval. Soon the salesperson begins treating

Ismail with more and more respect, trying to earn the one-blink affirmation that will get him or her a sale and commission.

Although eye blink is Ismail's primary means of communication these days, it's definitely not the only way he communicates. Teeth grinding is another one of his most important methods of communication. Ismail grinds his teeth whenever something is wrong, whenever he needs something urgently, or whenever he wants to "yell" at us because he's angry. It certainly gets our attention! The scraping of fingernails on a chalkboard sends chills up most people's backs. Ismail's grinding of teeth, so loud and urgent that it sounds as if his teeth are cracking, has the same effect on me and his nurses. It drives us up the wall! And that's its purpose.

Ismail has also learned how to make his ventilator beep by holding his breath to build up pressure in the ventilator circuit until the high pressure alarm sounds. He has a special code. If the ventilator beeps once, it could be simply a temporary high pressure in the circuit, but if it beeps twice in a row, Ismail is summoning us.

He also communicates a lot with his face and eyes, pointing at objects with his eyes to call our attention to something. When I get home late, he stares at the clock, and I know I'm being lectured for being gone too long. He points to the kitchen with his eyes to remind us that it is time for his water or his dinner. His animated facial expressions—smiles, laughs, icy stares, looks of surprise or excitement—speak volumes.

Ongoing Search for Technologies

Ismail once wrote an entire screenplay by using an infrared switch attached to his glasses that he operated by blinking his eye. The switch triggered the selection of letters and numbers on an alphabet grid, similar to the chart Ismail and I use in our day-to-day communications. The program had word prediction, which made sentence-building faster, and a voice synthesizer that could, if Ismail selected the right key, speak words he typed or that we had programmed into the system. The software program and voice synthesizer Ismail used were the same ones Stephen Hawking uses, so everything Ismail said sounded like the famous physicist! Unfortunately, using the infrared switch eventually became too difficult for Ismail and he stopped using this system.

As helpful as Ismail's eye blink has been to us over the years, we know there may come a time when Ismail could lose his ability to reliably blink his eye and will no longer be able to use this method of communication. So we are constantly on the lookout for new technologies.

Eye Gaze - Hope for the Future

Ismail has tried using a couple of different eye gaze systems. These devices contain a speech generating system, computer and sometimes an environmental control unit. With these systems, the user selects letters and numbers by gazing at them for a selected period of time (usually a fraction of a second) to spell words and then trigger the machine to read the typed words out loud. The user can also select icons or images on various screens that trigger the voice synthesizer to speak words and phrases that the user has programmed into the system. Both of the devices Ismail has tried are excellent, powerful systems that have worked for others. Unfortunately, they have not worked well for him.

One of the major challenges with these devices is setting up the equipment and positioning it precisely each time it is used. The device must be perfectly aligned and calibrated to track eye movement. Each time Ismail moves to a different position, the device has to be moved and readjusted too. It can sometimes be challenging to position the device exactly right so that it will work properly every time.

Wearable Communication Devices

In a review I wrote for Amazon.com for a book called *Age of Context: Mobile, Sensors, Data and the Future of Privacy*, by Robert Scoble and Shel Israel (**http://www.amazon.com/review/RCDKD5X9CZO83**), I pointed out that what is most exciting to me about Google Glass (digital eyewear that is worn like a pair of glasses and responds to voice commands) is its potential to be an electronic personal assistant and communication system for people with physical disabilities and communication challenges. Ever since learning about Google Glass, I have dreamed that someone would take the technology a step further and develop eye gaze technology to incorporate into a Google Glass-type wearable device. It didn't take long for my dream to come true!

EyeSpeak: Cutting Edge Eye Gaze Technology

EyeSpeak, new and exciting eye tracking augmented reality glasses, are being developed by LusoVU, a company in Lisbon, Portugal. Ivo Vieira, the company's CEO, has a PhD in physics engineering and has been working in the space sector for 16 years. Since 2002 he has been CEO of LusoSpace, a company that develops space technology. In February 2013, Vieira's father was diagnosed with ALS and is no longer able to speak. Vieira wanted to help his father and thousands of other people speak again. He and his team are using technology that is used for astronauts to develop augmented reality glasses that are specially designed for people with ALS, muscular dystrophy, and spinal cord injury, as well as those who have other disabilities affecting their communication abilities, such as "locked in" syndrome.

Still in development, EyeSpeak glasses are being designed to project a virtual keyboard onto the user's field of view while a micro camera, built into the glasses, track which keys the user is selecting with his or her eyes. The user's eyes will then be able to select the "speak" button, and a synthesized voice will speak what has been written through a speaker integrated into the glasses. A computer can also be connected to the device, allowing the user to control the mouse with his or her eyes. Since the glasses are worn on the face, they can be used in any position and will rarely require repositioning or re-calibrating.

In July 2014, LusoVU was successful in meeting its goal to raise $115,000 in 30 days through its Kickstarter campaign to help the company complete development of this technology and get the product to market. Ismail and I pledged funds to back the project, and Ismail will be an Early Adopter of EyeSpeak. We expect shipment of his device in March 2015. We have high hopes that EyeSpeak will open a new world of eye gaze communication to Ismail, but we will continue to watch for new technologies as well.

Technologies on the Horizon

In their book *Age of Context*, Scoble and Israel discuss a project that rewires a cockroach brain and straps a little Wi-Fi-enabled backpack to the bug so it can be controlled with an iPhone. Science fiction? Not any longer! "At first, the concept of wearable technology for roaches seemed too bizarre to cover here," Scoble and Israel explain, "but then we started considering the seven million people in the United States who suffer from such neural disorders as Parkinson's, Alzheimer's, cerebral palsy and multiple sclerosis. Perhaps the 'RoboRoaches,' as the researchers dubbed them, will lead to cures for serious neurology afflictions."

Augmentative communication technology has been exploring brain wave technology for some time. With the assistance of a computer and some electrodes, Ismail could potentially merely think a word, and it will be magically typed on a screen! We'll all be able to read Ismail's mind! There's a frightening thought!

Finding New Ways to Eat

Ismail and Cheryl enjoying dinner with Phil and Jane

As my ALS progressed, it became difficult for me to chew and swallow regular food or any form of liquid. One of my nurses came up with an idea to cook foods that didn't require much chewing. For breakfast, she used to prepare well-cooked spinach with two poached eggs. For lunch, she made a peanut butter and jelly sandwich on a piece of bread without the crust. For dinner, she cooked mashed potatoes mixed with half and half and butter. Then, Cheryl found a non-chew cookbook full of recipes for beverages, soups, casseroles, soufflés, desserts, and many other soft-food dishes that were tasty and didn't require chewing. The recipes she made from that cookbook gave me a good variety of nutritious food.

My ability to continue to eat by mouth lasted for a couple

of years. Then my condition grew worse until I was not able to swallow anything without choking.

Eating With the Help of a Tube

Cheryl called our family doctor and made an appointment. The doctor recommended we install a gastronomy feeding tube (G-tube) that would allow my nurses to put liquid food into a syringe and push it directly into my stomach. During the preparation for the surgery, a young resident asked my doctor if he could do the procedure. My doctor told him "not with this patient."

After the procedure, our doctor told me I should be given cans of liquid formula, like Ensure or Glucerna, for my meals. Liquid formula? I asked myself. How can I live on that? I love to eat! I had asked our family doctor to install the largest G-tube available. He did. I might be able to survive on nothing but cans of formula every day, but I didn't want to live like that.

Cheryl knew a doctor who was not only a medical doctor but was also a nutritionist. I saw him once before when I had a terrible cough. I had seen other doctors, but no one could help me, and the cough wouldn't go away. This doctor gave me advice on what to eat and drink to get rid of my cough. After a few days on the doctor's diet, the cough went away. After that, I trusted this doctor very much.

When we went to see him the following week and explained my situation to him, I listened carefully to what he had to say. He strongly recommended that my diet include kiwi fruit and raw sunflower seeds. He said these were two of the best foods I could eat. Cheryl did some research and found out that fresh, raw kiwi is a good source of dietary fiber, Vitamin E, Potassium, Copper, Vitamin C, and Vitamin K, and that raw sunflower seeds are an excellent source of protein, Vitamin E, and Vitamin B6.

Adding More Food and Vitamins

In addition to the kiwi and sunflower seeds, we started adding other fruit, hardboiled eggs, and other proteins to my formula. Cheryl began to make homemade soup with meat, chicken or fish and lots of vegetables. She cooks a big pot of the soup for me every two weeks and pours it into several medium-sized plastic containers. She puts the containers in the freezer, and the nurses defrost portions of the soup as needed and blend it up until smooth. They add chicken stock if needed until the soup is thin enough to go through the syringe and my G-tube. This is what they give me through my G-tube for my dinner every night. The recipe for Cheryl's soup is included in the Appendix. It is delicious and very nutritious. And I even get to enjoy special dinners with my friends.

After a few years, I was diagnosed with diverticulitis and could no longer eat kiwi or any other fruit with small seeds (such as strawberries). I could also no longer eat whole seeds, but I refused to give up my raw sunflower seeds. I asked Cheryl to find a coffee or spice grinder. The machine she got ground up the seeds pretty well, but there were still chunks of seeds left over. She found a way, though, to make a kind of powder by putting the seeds through the grinder three times and then stirring them through a sieve to separate out the remaining chunks. Our nurses help with preparing my sunflower seeds. They store the powder in the refrigerator in covered plastic containers to keep it fresh. Even today, my main diet consists of formula, sunflower seed powder, fruit, hardboiled eggs, other protein, and homemade soup. I also have one tablespoon of olive oil every day, which I think helps to keep my skin in good condition. You can read my daily menu in the Appendix.

In addition to the medications prescribed by my doctors, I take vitamin supplements every day. A list of the vitamin supplements I take is also in the Appendix.

With nutritious food, excellent nursing care, and lots of love from Cheryl, family, and friends, life is good, and I continue to stay healthy and happy.

Strangers in Our House

Ismail spells a message to one of his nurses

One of the most difficult adjustments we had to make when Ismail went on a ventilator was learning to live with nurses in our house nearly every waking minute of our lives. Ismail and I both had been private people and enjoyed our quiet times together. Suddenly, there were no quiet times.

Strangers were around us every minute of every day, from seven in the morning until eleven at night, watching everything we did, listening to everything we said. We missed having quiet, intimate moments. Whenever we needed to have a private husband and wife conversation, we had to wait until after 11:00 p.m. to grab a minute of privacy or ask Ismail's nurse to leave us alone for a few minutes and then close the door to our bedroom or office.

Since I worked outside the house every weekday, I felt uncomfortable leaving valuables or private papers lying around the house, where someone I barely knew could easily have access to them. In the early years, when I didn't know much about the nurses who were in our home, I conscientiously put those kinds of things out of sight. With time, however, I learned that I had little to worry about. The nursing agencies do background checks on all of their nurses, and we are now using agencies that we trust.

Fortunately, we have never had the kind of problems with Ismail's nurses that some families have had with caregivers they hire themselves. Over the years, we have developed a mutual trust with our nurses. The only incident I know of where a nurse ever stole anything in our home was the one time a nurse took some pills that had been prescribed for Ismail. The nurse was fired by the agency as soon as the problem was discovered.

As nurses began to stay longer on our case, we not only got used to their presence, we also began to welcome and enjoy it. Many of Ismail's nurses have been with us for years, some for more than 10 years, a couple for close to 20 years. They have become part of our extended family. We love them and care about them, just as they love and care about us. Of course, even in the closest of families, people can inadvertently hurt one another's feelings or get on each other's nerves. Whenever one of our nurses does or says something that annoys me or forgets to do something he or she was supposed to do, whenever someone breaks something, or drives Ismail's wheelchair into a wall, I tell myself "Don't sweat the small stuff." Words can be forgotten, mistakes can be corrected, cracked walls can be repaired and broken objects replaced. But what would I do without Ismail's wonderful nurses? It's now difficult for me to imagine what the house would be like without their presence. Quiet and lonely. I would miss them and their companionship, their chatter, their advice.

Selecting a new nurse is like making a new friend. Outstanding professional experience and excellent skills are essential, but so are good attitude and pleasant personality. New nurses not only have to provide exceptional care to Ismail, but also have to fit into our "family." They have to be willing to work hard and help out one another. They have to be punctual and reliable. Our insurance company pays for two 8-hour nursing shifts per day: 7:00 a.m. to 3:00 p.m. and 3:00 p.m. to 11:00 p.m. We need to have an adequate number of back-up nurses who can fill in when others request time off, or who can do overnight shifts whenever I go out of town.

For many years, we had a major problem filling all of the nursing shifts that were prescribed for Ismail's care. I came to believe that it was impossible for one nursing agency to provide enough qualified nurses to fill all of the required sixteen hours of care, seven days a week. If a shift didn't get filled, I had to provide the care myself until a qualified nurse could be scheduled. The nursing agencies we use today work very hard to get all of our shifts filled. That was not always the case.

For some of the agencies we used in the past, providing nursing care was simply a business. If they didn't make a certain profit margin, it wasn't worth it to them to provide the service. They often paid lower hourly wages to their nurses than other agencies did, which meant they didn't always have the best, most reliable nurses on their roster, and they tended to have a lot of staff turnover. Nurses would work for them, and in turn, for us, until they were able to find work with other agencies that paid them higher salaries and/or provided better benefits. Some agencies had the attitude that if they had a nurse to send, they'd be happy to provide us with one. If they didn't, they wouldn't. There were times I had to provide care for many shifts in a week, sometimes back-to-back, even two or three days in a row. I dreaded holidays because the agencies rarely had nurses to send on those days. During one particularly bad time, I was doing more hours of care in a month than the nurses were providing.

Our insurance company became concerned about the large number of unfilled nurses' shifts. After meeting with the nursing agency, Ismail's previous and current pulmonologists, and us, our insurance company decided to try something I had been begging it to do for years: contract with two nursing agencies simultaneously. This, I always believed, would double our pool of potential nurses and motivate both agencies to work harder to recruit and train new nurses for our case so that they could get the business. This decision and the resulting positive outcome was a major victory for Ismail and me. It was the turning point in our home care experience. We were finally able to fill almost all of our open shifts—almost all of the time, even on holidays—for the first time since agencies started sending nurses to our home.

In the many years we have been using our two current agencies, we have never had a major problem or serious incident that would jeopardize their business relationship and professional performance. Everyone works together to make sure we have the number of nursing hours that have been prescribed by Ismail's physician and that all of our nurses are well-trained and good fits for our case.

Of course, there are times when nurses leave us because of a problem or change in their lives: they move out of the area, go back to school full-time, get married, get pregnant, accept a full-time position with a hospital, etc., etc. When good things happen to our nurses, we are happy, even though it means we'll be losing them. We care about them and want them to be happy and successful. Still, losing a good nurse is always traumatic, and Ismail and I go through a grieving process because we are losing a cherished member of our extended family. Then the time-consuming, often painful cycle of recruiting and training a new nurse—and transforming that new stranger in our house to a loved and trusted member of our extended family—begins again.

Growing Pains: Building and Training a Nursing Team

Ismail with three of his nurses and team mascot "Lou"

One of the ongoing and most difficult problems for Cheryl and me is finding and training new nurses. When I first started using the ventilator Cheryl and I did not know what my caregiving needs were, and we did not know much about the respiratory equipment. Cheryl had to learn very quickly how to operate the ventilator and suctioning equipment. She had to know how to troubleshoot problems that might occur.

We didn't know what to expect or what was customary or acceptable when agencies first started sending nurses to our home to take care of me. We believed that the agency would always send qualified nurses and that we were required to accept the nurses they sent. We soon discovered that sometimes the agencies we used back then said their nurses were great, but we didn't always agree. Some of these nurses not only did not know how to operate the respiratory equipment, but I doubt they had ever seen a ventilator. And forget being able to suction my trachea!

The Good, the Bad, and the Dangerous

I like and respect all of my caregivers. They are dedicated to their profession of nursing, and most of them have been with me for many years. Sometimes, however, new nurses have had poor attitudes or were not well trained to handle my needs.

The Nurse Who Made Me Pass Out

Once an agency sent a nurse who was supposed to have had over thirty years of experience in nursing and assured us that he was well qualified. He accidentally disconnected me from the ventilator. The ventilator's alarm went off and kept beeping. When he didn't reconnect me, I started grinding my teeth to let him know something was wrong. He froze and couldn't figure out what was the matter. I passed out. Luckily, another nurse was coming on duty at that time. She figured out the problem and reconnected me. Thanks to her, I recovered.

The Nurse Who Ignored My Coughing

A new nurse once came in, introduced himself, sat down in a chair, opened a book, and started reading. He paid no attention to me, even after I started coughing rather hard. My coughing did not disturb his reading. Since this was soon after I went on a ventilator, I was still able to talk at that time. I asked him to suction me, but he did not disturb himself to do so. Eventually, my coughing stopped. When the afternoon nurse finally came on duty, she suctioned me. I asked her to call the agency for me. I talked to the Director of Nurses and explained to her what was happening. She promised that she would send my Case Manager out to meet with me and that she would send better nurses.

The next morning, the Case Manager arrived at my video production office, where I still worked. I was coughing, but the nurse ignored me, continuing to read. The Case Manager asked him why he wasn't suctioning me. "It's just a cough," he replied. "It will stop in a minute."

The Case Manager was furious. She told him he should be more caring with his patient who needed his help He was fired without a recommendation.

The Nurse Who Stabbed Me

Another time, the agency sent a nurse who was very nice, but who was not experienced with the ventilator or with how to properly suction. I was in pain every time she suctioned me. After she left for the night, Cheryl suctioned me and found a lot of blood in my trachea. She was upset and worried. After gently suctioning me a few times, the bleeding slowed down, then finally stopped.

She decided she still had to take me to urgent care the next morning to have me checked out. The same nurse came the next morning, and Cheryl told her what had happened. The nurse seemed very surprised. She came with us to the urgent care clinic. She was a very large nurse. I felt sorry for her because she could not get into the van. Cheryl had to have her stand on the van's wheelchair lift and have the lift raise her up so she could get into the van.

In the clinic, the doctor put a scope down my trachea. "It's your suctioning technique," he told Cheryl and the nurse. He had them look into the scope. Cheryl said she saw many cuts on the inside of my trachea where the nurse had repeatedly stabbed me with the tip of the suction catheter. When Cheryl told the agency what had happened, the nursing supervisor said she wouldn't blame us if we didn't want to have the nurse back. We told her not to send her again.

The Nurse Who Doped Me Up

Once I had a nurse who was giving me a wrong medication that made me sleep all day. I tried to tell her that what she was giving me was an incorrect medication. Either she would not listen to me or she did not know medications. In other ways, she was a good nurse, and I liked her. After a few weeks, I had to let her go. I had caught up on my sleeping and was very well rested.

The Nurse Who Called 911

A new nurse was sent by an agency one day while Cheryl was at work. She didn't know how to transfer me with the Hoyer lift. When she tried, she got me in a bad position in my wheelchair and couldn't get me pulled up to a good position. She called 911 for help. Fire trucks and paramedics rushed to our house. The paramedics helped her get me into my wheelchair. The next day, one of our other nurses told us they saw a story about what happened in the local newspaper. The agency was very upset and never sent her to our home again.

The Nurse Who Roughed Me Up

A new nurse was shaving me. She pressed the shaver too hard on my face, and it was hurting me. I asked her to stop pressing so hard. Not only did she ignore me, but she got angry and continued pressing hard as she shaved me. Later, I asked her to feed me my breakfast. My swallowing was getting weak at that time. I could still swallow food, but I needed someone to place the food into my mouth, and it took me a long time to eat. The nurse was pushing forks full of food into my mouth very hard and very fast. I started choking on the food. I asked her why she was feeding me so fast. "I'm not going to take all day to feed you," she replied.

Later that morning, I asked her to give me some water. She didn't move or say anything. I waited for the next nurse to bring me some water. When Cheryl came home that night, I suggested she fill up a thermos with juice and put a long straw in it. I asked her to place the thermos with the straw near where I sat during the day so I could sip the juice myself.

The next morning, the same nurse started to give me range of motion exercises so hard that I asked her to stop because I could not take the pain. She brushed my teeth very hard, too, and I had to ask her to stop. Later, I figured out that she was doing these things intentionally. She would do anything to save a few seconds of work, and she was taking away my right to good care. When I asked her why she was doing this, she said, "I am here to watch you and not serve you." Cheryl and I made sure that was her last day as my caregiver.

The Nurses Who Abandoned Me

Our nurses are scheduled for two eight-hour shifts. One day, the nurse who was supposed to come at 3:00 p.m. was late. The morning nurse was anxious to leave. She had a little baby, and she was worried about her babysitter. The nurse who was supposed to be there at 3:00 p.m. called to tell her she would be late. When the morning nurse complained, the other nurse told her to leave. Cheryl was not home, and the nurse said she couldn't leave me by myself. However, the afternoon nurse told her that she was an R.N., and since the morning nurse was only an L.V.N. she needed to do what she told her to do.

The nursing agency then called and told the morning nurse to leave because they were not going to pay her overtime if she stayed beyond her scheduled hours. So, the nurse left me by myself. I asked myself what would happen if I became disconnected from the ventilator. As time went by, I became more and more afraid.

After a long while, the afternoon nurse arrived, smiling. "Nothing happened to you," she told me. "Everything is okay."

I told her not to come back any more. She got upset and left. I was again all by myself. Fortunately, soon after that, Cheryl came home. She had been contacted by the agency and told that I was all alone because the nurses had left. She was really, really angry.

Changing Needs and Better Care

After a while, the agency started sending more caring, better-qualified nurses. What we did not know was these nurses needed special training to familiarize themselves with my particular needs. The agency's Case Manager suggested that new nurses come for an orientation before starting to work. She suggested four hours of training in each of two shifts, for a total of eight hours.

The agency sent three new nurses the following week. One of them was unacceptable, but the other two were experienced and compassionate and had taken care of other ALS patients in the past. They knew how to operate the ventilator and troubleshoot problems. They knew how to suction. Besides their main nursing duties, they went out of their way to make my everyday life pleasant and happy. They did little things, such as massage my neck and feet; they were great caregivers for me.

As time went on, I lost my speech and the ability to stand up for manual transfers. It became increasingly difficult for me to swallow food and liquid, and I became more and more dependent on Cheryl and the nurses. We had to find a way for me to be transferred from my wheelchair to my bed and to the commode. We also had to find a way for me to communicate with all of my caregivers. This situation made it more difficult for Cheryl and the nurses to take care of me. It meant that new nurses needed more training.

The nursing agency did not want to go to the expense of paying for more training for their nurses. We had to explain to them that my care had changed, and I needed more experienced nurses. It took Cheryl a lot of negotiating, but finally the agency agreed to extend new nurses' training to three eight-hour shifts, a total of 24 hours of training.

Often 24 hours of training is still not enough for a new nurse to learn everything he or she needs to know to take good care of me. There are many things my nurses need to do. A list of my nurses' duties can be found in the Appendix. It is a long list.

In addition, all my nurses need to know how to take me to doctors' and dentists' appointments and go on outings with me and Cheryl. This includes strapping me into my wheelchair and adjusting my headrest so my head is held securely in place during transport, using a lift to raise me and my chair into the van, positioning my wheelchair properly, and tying down my wheelchair with the straps on the van's floor.

You can see why my nurses have to be quick learners! Some nurses find the routine and number of duties overwhelming.

Our Ongoing Search

Gradually, things started to settle down. We had nurses who stayed with us for many years and who took great care of me. Of course, from time to time there are occasions when a nurse leaves our case, and we have to train someone new. Occasionally, a nurse cannot successfully finish the training, and the agency will have to send another nurse. The nursing agencies we use now are careful about screening their nurses and sending those who have good experience and skills and are committed to staying on our case.

New Nurses Can Be Scary

To this day, having new nurses come to take care of me is stressful, sometimes scary. I worry that I might not able to communicate with my new nurse if there's an emergency or that the nurse might not be able to troubleshoot a ventilator problem when I am not getting any air. Sometimes a new nurse who hasn't yet learned the suctioning technique my caregivers use for me are not able to adequately suction me or can injure me with his or her suctioning technique. I'm also afraid of a new nurse dropping me or letting me fall during a transfer.

To avoid these potential dangers, Cheryl and my nurses focus on several important skills when we train new nurses, including eye blink communication with my alphabet chart, ventilator training and how to troubleshoot problems with the ventilator equipment, trachea and oral suctioning techniques, and safe transferring techniques with my Hoyer lift.

Unfortunately, these are often the skills that are the most difficult for new nurses to learn. It takes time and patience on everyone's part to train new nurses who want to take care of me.

To make sure that every new nurse understands what minimum skills are required, Cheryl developed a list of expectations that we give to every new nurse on their first day of orientation. The document says:

Minimum skills requirements for all caregivers:

1. Ability to communicate with Ismail. This involves learning to use the communication chart and spelling with Ismail via eye blink. It also involves getting to know and accurately interpret his other nonverbal communication methods (i.e., eye gaze, facial expressions).
2. Knowledge of the ventilator. This involves being completely comfortable with Ismail's ventilator

model, knowing what the appropriate settings are and which ones can be adjusted by us. It also involves knowing how to set up and clean the circuitry. Most important, it involves knowing how to troubleshoot a problem and what to do in case of an emergency.

3. Ability to suction Ismail correctly and safely. This involves becoming skilled in the special suctioning technique we use for Ismail.

4. Ability to transfer Ismail unassisted to and from the bed and the commode.

5. Good judgment and common sense, including acting calmly and effectively under pressure and in emergencies.

Probation Period

For a new nurse's first couple of shifts, Cheryl stays home to monitor everything, answer questions, help troubleshoot, and assist with communication. She will not leave a nurse alone with me until she, the nurse, and I all feel comfortable that I will be safe and that the nurse can handle everything on her or his own. This was sometimes hard for Cheryl when she was working full time and either had to request a day off of work to stay home with us, or schedule the nurse's first few shifts on her days off.

My Awesome Team

We have been fortunate to be able to build a team of excellent, caring, and reliable nurses. I am grateful that most of them have been taking care of me for many years and understand my needs very well. They also care about me as a person as well as a patient and do everything they can to make me happy. I am very lucky to have such wonderful nurses. I feel safe with them and enjoy being with them. I consider them my friends.

Surrounding Ismail with Positive Attitudes

Ismail, Cheryl, Phil, and Jane, January 2014

Some people have a problem interacting with individuals with disabilities. They feel awkward around the person, not knowing what to say, how to act, afraid to touch them, even on the hand or the shoulder. They may be frightened. They may think, "This could happen to me. To my wife. To my children." They are reminded that life is fragile, imperfect, unpredictable. So they retreat. It saddens me that Ismail lost a number of what he considered close friends when he began to show signs of paralysis and an inability to speak clearly because of ALS. Losing these friends was painful for Ismail, but it also caused him to treasure even more those special friends who have continued to love and support him throughout the progression of his disease. Dear lifelong friends such as Phil and Jane and Sherry and her husband, John D'Attile, have always been like family.

I insist on surrounding Ismail with friendly, supportive people. I invite into our home only those who respect and interact with Ismail, who smile at him and talk to him. I apply this requirement not only to friends and neighbors, but also to gardeners, housekeepers, plumbers, painters, contractors, and other service people as well. The first time someone comes into our home to discuss their product or service I bring them over to Ismail and introduce them to him. I explain that Ismail has ALS and what that means. I tell them that Ismail is not able to speak, but communicates with eye blink, that one blink means "yes" and two blinks means "no." I inform them that Ismail must give his approval to whatever they are trying to sell us. Those who smile at Ismail, make eye contact with him, speak directly to him and include him in discussions get invited back. Those who don't, don't.

Finding Doctors with Positive Attitudes

I use the same criteria when selecting Ismail's health care providers. I look for doctors who not only have excellent credentials and experience, but who also treat Ismail with that all-important friendly, caring attitude—and respect. Ismail uses the same criteria. I recall an incident many years ago when a Neurology resident came into an exam room and, right in front of Ismail, began asking me questions about him and his condition instead of addressing Ismail himself. Realizing the doctor knew nothing about ALS, although the specialty in which he was training was Neurology, I smiled and explained to him that Ismail was able to communicate and could answer his questions by blinking "yes" or "no." Continuing to act as if Ismail weren't even in the room, the resident proceeded to talk to me instead of to him, asking me all the questions that Ismail should have been answering.

After a few minutes, Ismail started angrily grinding his teeth and looked at me with an expression that said "I'm mad, and I have something to say." I asked the resident to wait a moment while I found out what Ismail wanted to spell out. "I have ALS," he began spelling, his face red and tense with anger. "I am not stupid. You are stupid." The resident walked out of the room and never returned. Good riddance.

I also make sure we select doctors who have an optimistic outlook and a willingness to treat Ismail's health issues with the same amount of aggressiveness when appropriate as they would other patients who don't have ALS. Ismail is "full code", which means that should his heart stop beating, we would want his doctors to do everything possible to revive him.

Some doctors expect people with ALS to die within a couple of years and decide it might be counter-productive to treat potentially life-threatening conditions. They are quick to say, "He's not a candidate for surgery," thereby closing the door to many treatment options. Of course, it's true that surgery can be more complicated, sometimes risky or downright dangerous, for Ismail and others with ALS whose health is compromised or who use ventilators. I understand that physicians weigh the benefits with the risks of surgery and often feel the risks outweigh the benefits. Still, that doesn't necessarily mean that surgery can't be an option. In two instances, when we were originally told that Ismail was not a candidate for surgery, he went on to have surgical procedures that most likely saved his life.

The Flat Polyp

During a routine colonoscopy a few years ago, Ismail's gastroenterologist discovered a flat polyp that was in a very advanced stage and was highly likely to become malignant. I asked the GI resident who had called to give me the report what the treatment would be. He told me that normally the surgical team would do a resection of the colon to make certain they removed all of the polyp but, because of Ismail's condition, "He is…" wait for it…"not a candidate for surgery." The resident said there was no plan to treat the polyp. No plan! "This type of polyp is slow-growing," he went on to explain. "It will probably take a year or two for it to grow enough to cause a problem." A year or two! The GI team would do follow-up colonoscopies, and "keep an eye on it."

"What's the purpose of 'keeping an eye it?'" I asked angrily, "if you don't plan to treat it?"

"To make sure the polyp doesn't eventually cause a bowel obstruction or other problem." He added that they may remove part of it from time to time if it grows too big.

"I need to speak with the gastroenterologist," I told him, refusing to allow Ismail to die unnecessarily of colon cancer.

I told the gastroenterologist that I was not comfortable with him not removing the polyp. It turned out that there is a technique called endoscopic mucosal resection that a physician with special training can use to remove flat polyps from the colon wall without invasive surgery. The gastroenterologist said he was trying to arrange for Ismail to have this procedure, but that it was not easy. There was only one surgeon he knew in the medical group who had special training in this technique, and because Ismail is on a ventilator, arrangements had to be made to have him admitted to the hospital for the procedure. It took many weeks of waiting and follow-up, but finally a surgery date was set. When the procedure was completed, the polyp had been successfully removed without complications. The surgeon did the required biopsy and sent it off to the lab. He told me that everything went fine.

I was relieved that the danger from the polyp was a thing of the past. When the surgeon called a few days later with the biopsy results, he said he was surprised that the lab reported finding some malignant tissue in the polyp. I was stunned. Afraid. In the time it took to wait for a specialist to agree to remove the polyp and for the procedure to be scheduled, the advanced polyp had already begun to become malignant. The surgeon reassured me that he was confident he had removed the entire polyp inside the colon. Unfortunately, there was no way to see if there was any growth outside the lining of the colon. Hopefully, he said, the malignancy was in a very early stage and was contained inside the polyp itself.

I scheduled a follow-up colonoscopy a few months later to make sure there was no evidence that the polyp had begun to grow back. Thankfully, the colonoscopy showed that it hadn't. A year later, Ismail had another colonoscopy. No sign of polyps! Thank God I stuck to my guns and demanded that Ismail's polyp be removed. I'm a big believer in stubbornness. In this case, my stubbornness most likely saved my husband's life.

The Power of Positive Energy

For Ismail and me, surrounding ourselves with love, friendliness, respect, good attitudes, and positive energy have brought happiness and good things our way! It has even contributed to extending Ismail's life.

Hot and Cold

Ismail's Supporters ALS Walk team, October 2011. Team members piled their jackets on Ismail's lap to help keep him warm.

Before ALS hit me, my body could endure all sorts of cold weather. In fact, I lived in many cold places, such as Detroit, Michigan, and New York. I even spent a winter in Ottawa, Canada. I remember one cold Saturday night in Ottawa when some of my friends and I went to see a Western movie. It was freezing cold that night. After the movie, we ran as fast as we could to my car. I pulled my car keys out of my pocket and tried to open the car door, but the key hole was frozen solid. I tried to force the key into the lock, but no such luck! My friends and I looked around for a telephone booth so we could call for help, but there were none around. There were no houses or shops nearby either, and no people around to help us.

One of my friends pulled out a pocket knife. He attempted to scrape the ice from the keyhole, but he broke the knife. We continued to look around for someone or something that could help us. Nothing. It was getting colder and colder. One of my friends was shivering. In desperation, I told my friends to form a circle around me. Once they did, I started to urinate into the keyhole of the car. After a few seconds, the ice melted and I was able to get the key into the keyhole and open the door. We piled into the car, turned on the heater, and went home.

I'm glad that I now live in Southern California because I could never again survive a cold night like that one in Ottawa. Because of ALS I no longer have enough muscle mass to keep my body warm, and I feel cold all the time. Eventually, it came to the point that I even felt cold in eighty-degree temperatures. It was too chilly for me at an October 2011 walk I participated in for the ALS Association. My thoughtful teammates took off their jackets and piled them on top of my lap to help me feel warmer. Our Ismail's Supporters team picture above shows me sitting under a big pile of jackets!

For me to feel comfortable these days, the temperature must be at least 85-90 degrees! I would love my house to be 85-90 degrees all year around. Unfortunately, Cheryl and my nurses do not have the same temperature requirements that I do. So, I have to compromise. Cheryl came up with an idea. She got two electric blankets for me. One is a full-size blanket that I use in bed at night. The other is an electric throw blanket that my nurses wrap around me when I'm in the wheelchair during the day. That way, the house can stay around 80 degrees (still warm for Cheryl and the nurses, but they have learned to tolerate it because they love me). I can stay warm with the blanket turned on high.

During Spring and Summer, when most days in Southern California are bright and warm—often good and hot—I ask my nurse to take me out to our patio so I can enjoy the outdoors. While my body soaks in the warmth of the sun, I look at the flowers, bushes, grass, and trees in my backyard. I enjoy the birds flying over me and perching on tree branches. I watch hummingbirds fly from flower to flower, drinking nectar. Occasionally, a squirrel runs along the top of our wall. Sometimes, one will stop to rest, draping its legs over the sides of the wall as it sunbathes along with me. I could stay in the sun all day. I probably would, if it wasn't for Cheryl and my nurses. They watch the clock and bring me back into the house before I get sunburned and overheated. Thanks to them, no heat strokes for me!

I wish it could be summer all year long. At least it feels like summer inside my house all year!

Adventures in Las Vegas

Above, Cheryl and Ismail's wedding portrait, November 26, 1970. At right, their 25-year renewal of wedding vows, November 23, 1995

To me, Las Vegas is a city of fun and adventure—and romance. I love the lights and the noise and Cirque du Soleil. I enjoy the hotel themes that let you travel to Paris, to ancient Egypt, to New York City, to Camelot all in one day. Las Vegas will always have a special place in my heart because it is the city in which Ismail and I were married—twice.

Growing up I dreamed, as so many American girls do, of a big church wedding with hundreds of guests and a floor-length frilly white dress. Of pomp and circumstance, a scene right out of a fairy tale. Then I met my Prince Charming and fell deeply in love. But as we began planning our wedding, I had trouble creating the rest of the fairy tale. Neither we nor my parents had the means to pay for a big wedding. My parents started talking about taking out a second mortgage on their home to pay for one. Instead, we decided to have a simple civil ceremony. But where? I couldn't completely abandon my dream of having a romantic wedding. A quick ceremony at a courthouse performed by a Justice of the Peace just wouldn't do. We could elope! To Las Vegas! I'd never been there. What a great opportunity to see Las Vegas and get married at the same time!

Fresh out of college, I had just started a new job and had no vacation time that I could use for a honeymoon. A more challenging problem was that neither Ismail nor I owned a car at the time. Hard to run away to get married without any transportation. To resolve the first problem, we scheduled our elopement for Thanksgiving weekend. I know, "scheduling an elopement" sounds like an oxymoron. My new boss generously gave me the Friday after Thanksgiving off. We could have a four-day honeymoon! My parents loaned us their car.

In Las Vegas, Ismail and I had the time of our lives. Our dear friends, Phil and Jane, were with us. Phil did all of the driving in my parents' car. He was Best Man, and Jane was Maid of Honor. Phil, a cinematographer, took our wedding pictures. We got married on Thanksgiving Day at the World Famous Chapel of the Bells. Then we all went out for a turkey dinner. It was 1970, prior to the construction of theme hotels, the days when hotels were simply hotels and casinos were casinos.

We stayed at The Tropicana. Since we had no money for shows, we spent most of our time at Circus Circus, watching trapeze artists swinging high above the tent-like casino (a poor man's version of Cirque du Soleil). We sat through a long presentation about property investment opportunities in Las Vegas, just so we could get a few casino chips the company was giving away as a gift for attending. Phil bet the chips he got in a game of Blackjack and won enough to pay for dinner for all of us that night. Luck was on our side!

We were married! We had a lifetime ahead of us — to be together and achieve our dreams! We were penniless now, but one day Ismail would be a successful movie director and I would be a novelist. The fairy tale was just beginning. We would live happily ever after.

We went back to Las Vegas to celebrate our tenth wedding anniversary. That was before ALS changed our lives. We still believed life would bring us all we dreamed of.

Every time we returned to Las Vegas after that, we came with nurses and a ventilator. The fairy tale had ended, and life had become more complicated. It took advanced planning and hard work now to take a vacation, but we still had fun, and we still had dreams. ALS was not going to take those away from us.

The last time we went to Las Vegas together, it was to renew our marriage vows on our twenty-fifth wedding anniversary. We had hoped to bring my parents along so they could finally witness our wedding, but my mother was preparing for hip surgery and was in a lot of pain. We thought it would be just the two of us and our nurse. We were moved to learn that our nurse's parents, who felt bad that my family could not be there to witness our vows, would be driving to Las Vegas to attend our ceremony. We couldn't believe the kindness and generosity of this wonderful couple. It was the first and last time we ever saw them, but their names are on our marriage certificate, so they will always be a part of our lives.

We renewed our vows at the same chapel in which we were married. But the Chapel of the Bells was not quite as we remembered it. It was dark the night we got married in 1970, and the neon lights of the chapel, outlining a bell, looked romantic. Now, when we pulled up to the chapel in 1995, daylight revealed a sleazy-looking Fun City Motel next door that I didn't remember and a large roller coaster ride. Inside the chapel, our simple ceremony was beautiful and full of special meaning. At the end of it, the minister, apparently moved by our continuing love and devotion to one another despite adversity, fought back tears.

Wheels

Ismail participating in the 2014 Walk to Defeat ALS

When I started to use the ventilator, our insurance company paid for a very good manual wheelchair with a tray at the bottom to hold my ventilator. We had to wait a while for it because it was custom made. We didn't have a van at the time, but I could ride in the front seat of our small car, and the ventilator could be strapped with a seat belt behind me in the back seat. Once I was inside the car, the wheelchair could be disassembled and stored in the trunk. When we got to our destination, Cheryl could pull the pieces of the chair out of the trunk and put it together again. If we had to stop at several places, Cheryl got a lot of exercise putting the wheelchair together and taking it apart over and over.

Because it was a manual wheelchair, it was difficult for Cheryl and the nurses to maneuver, especially going up and down hills. One time we took a nurse with us to Carmel-by-the-Sea, a beautiful little village near Monterey, California. Carmel has a lot of hills. Cheryl and the nurse had to each grab onto a handle at the back of the chair and push as hard as they could to get the wheelchair up the hills. Then, they had to both struggle to slow the chair down every time we went down the hills.

On another occasion, we were going down a hill at Disneyland, and the nurse was having trouble slowing down the wheelchair. "Look out!" she yelled at the people below us. "Get out of the way!"

Holding onto the chair's handles, she ran behind the chair, unable to slow it down. "Wheelchair coming! Get out of the way!" People were running all around, trying to get out of my path. I was relieved when we finally got to the bottom of the hill without running over anybody. My nurse was out-of-breath, frazzled and exhausted.

Another time we were at the Los Angeles Zoo. I never noticed before how many hills the zoo has! The chair got out of the hands of the nurse and started speeding down a hill by itself. I was scared that the chair might turn over and break my arm or my leg. Or, my neck. It might even break my ventilator!

The nurse was even more scared than I was. She kept running behind the chair and screaming "Oh, my God!" When the chair finally stopped at the bottom of the hill, she grabbed it and asked me if I was all right. Her eyes were big, and she was out of breath. I was okay, and I was glad we got down another hill without running over anybody. Unfortunately, I lost many nurses who refused to come back to take care of me because they could not handle my wheelchair.

Eventually, we were able to purchase a van at a special price from the State of California, and the State also helped us pay for the modifications that were needed to put a wheelchair lift in the van and some straps to secure my wheelchair for traveling.

After a while, my insurance company supplied me with a beautiful power wheelchair. I was then totally mobile with my power chair and brand new handicap van!

The same day I got my new power chair, our friend Phil arrived from New York at Los Angeles International Airport for a visit. None of us knew how to drive my new chair, but we decided to take it anyway. We arrived at the airport at a busy time, in the middle of a lot of traffic. Cheryl parked the van in a lot across from where Phil's plane was arriving.

We had a great nurse with us, but because she was just learning how to drive my wheelchair, she had trouble getting it out of the van. She finally got me out and then had difficulty driving the chair. She kept complaining that it was too fast, but she didn't know how to slow it down. We tried to cross the street that was full of cars going to various terminals and picking up and dropping off passengers.

We waited for the light to change. When it did, the traffic stopped and we started to cross the street. My chair started speeding ahead. The nurse was trying to steer it, but it was out of control, zigzagging wildly in front of the traffic. Then the nurse lost hold of the chair, and it started spinning around in the middle of the street. I was getting dizzy. I was also scared that we'd be hit by a car or that the chair might tip over and I would get hurt or the ventilator would get damaged. The light changed again, and cars started coming toward us. They would approach us and then stop abruptly before hitting us. Finally, we made it across the street. We greeted Phil and brought him home with us for a nice visit.

The next day, someone from the wheelchair company came out and took a look at the wheelchair. Somehow, the speed control had been set at the very highest level. He showed Cheryl and the nurse how to readjust the speed.

The walls of our house became full of scratches and gouges from nurses running into them with the chair. Cheryl had to call a contractor to repair our walls. Then they got scratched and gouged again. Even today, our walls have scratches from the wheelchair, but we have learned to live with them. Occasionally, we cover them with a fresh coat of paint. Having a power wheelchair is worth it.

Battling Pressure Sores

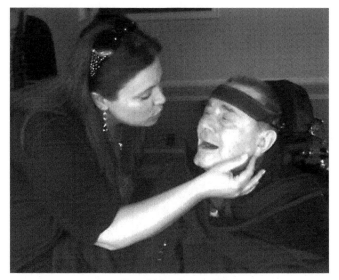

Ismail and his niece, Hollen

We have an ongoing war with pressure sores. There are four stages of these painful, potentially dangerous wounds: In stage 1, the skin may appear red, but there are no breaks or tears. In stage 2, the skin is open or ulcerated. In stage 3, the injury extends into the tissue beneath the skin. In stage 4, the injury involves the muscle and sometimes the bone. Stage 4 wounds can cause damage to deeper tissues, tendons, and joints. Pressure sores can develop quickly and often take a long time to heal. In some severe cases, they never heal. Infection of the bone or blood can occur if advanced stage pressure sores progress, sometimes causing death.

Somehow, Ismail's skin went from being smooth and perfect and beautiful for many years to becoming plagued with frequent skin breakdowns. We'd get one sore healed, and another would develop somewhere else. As soon as that one healed, the first one would open up again. Ismail's doctors and nurses all said the same thing: Ismail had to get out of his wheelchair and off of his wounds for them to heal.

As I've mentioned previously, Ismail is a stubborn man. A very stubborn man. Once he was out of bed in the morning, there was no way he was going to get back into bed that day. He wanted to stay active and in the midst of things. He believed that staying out of bed was one of the things that helped him survive so many years. He knew of other people with ALS who developed pneumonia because they stayed in bed all the time. He would rather have an open wound than stay in bed. So for many years, we struggled with Ismail's pressure sores. We tried many different creams and ointments, sought the advice of wound care experts ("Keep him in bed and off of the sore," they'd always say). We spoke to his doctors ("Keep him off the sore," they'd advise). I browsed through home health catalogs and went to expositions that displayed products and equipment for people with disabilities, always hunting for a miracle cream that would heal Ismail's wounds.

Seemingly overnight, one of his wounds advanced from a chronic stage 2 to a stage 4. The wound was huge and deep, all the way to the bone. I was terrified. The wound care specialist who was sent out to our home was worried about possible bone infection. She asked the doctor to order a bone x-ray and scan. Thankfully, the results were negative.

We had to act fast before infection set in. We began an aggressive treatment plan. I rented a second hospital bed, which we set up in our family room, in front of the television set and in the midst of family activity. We convinced Ismail to lie down in it for a few hours every afternoon. We set up an alternating air pressure mattress on the bed, and the nurses frequently turned him to get pressure off the wound.

Our insurance company paid for a low air loss mattress for Ismail to sleep on at night. This mattress is recommended for patients with stage 3 and stage 4 wounds and assists in the healing process.

We diligently nursed his wound and watched it slowly...ever so slowly...grow smaller. Ismail became obsessed with the progress of the healing, asking nurses for a report, including measurements, every time they changed the dressing. He got into the bed in the family room every day without complaint, and even began to enjoy his afternoon naps. Little by little the stage 4 wound healed. The nurses, the doctors, and the wound care expert were all amazed. Some admitted they had doubted it would ever heal. They warned us that the wound has a "memory" and can easily open up again if we are not extremely careful.

We are determined that what Ismail's doctors and nurses will always consider a Stage 4 pressure sore will never advance to that dangerous condition again. Keeping an eye on the wound site and taking immediate action at the first sign of breakdown is an ongoing priority for all of us.

Working With My Feet

Ismail operating his video editing equipment using foot controls

As my disease progressed, it robbed me of the use of my hands and arms and neck. I couldn't keep my head straight. It would fall forward, and my chin would hit my chest. My brain and my will would give orders to my hands and my arms to move, but the ALS disobeyed. I went to see a neurologist. He could not do anything for my hands and arms, but he prescribed a neck brace to hold my head straight.

I could no longer operate my video editing equipment. I was losing my clients one by one. I got very worried that I was going to lose my video post-production business.

Cheryl heard about a conference that was being held in the beautiful city of Santa Barbara, California, which is about 70 miles from our home. The conference was conducted by a group of engineers who helped people with disabilities and by some students who were majoring in engineering. It was focused on helping people with disabilities. We entered the conference with great hopes. After a few minutes our hope turned to disappointment. The engineers could design artificial prostheses to help people who had lost their arms or legs, but could not help someone in my condition.

Cheryl drove us home. All that night I was unable to sleep. My disappointment and fear of losing my business made it impossible for me to relax. The following week, Cheryl did some research and found out that a program through the State of California might help us with making modifications to my video editing equipment. At that point, my legs and feet were still very strong, and the state wanted to keep every able person working as long as possible. Cheryl contacted the state and after a few days someone from the program called to make an appointment. One of their engineers would come to my office to check out my video editing equipment. I was skeptical at first. After he checked the equipment, he tried to explain what he was going to do, but I was still skeptical.

A week went by and we had not heard from him. I was beginning to think we never would. However, he showed up at my office with a bag a few days later. He opened the bag and pulled out two rectangular wooden boards. One of the boards contained a controller with a ball and the other contained two switch plates. Attached to the back of the boards were wires that he attached to the editing controller of my equipment. He demonstrated with his own foot that he could roll the ball every which way to run my video players and recorder. He could mark the beginning and end of an edit by pressing the switch plates with his other foot. It was like using a giant trackball that could be operated with feet instead of a hand.

Once he demonstrated how it worked, he had me practice. He stayed with me for a few hours until I learned how to do it. At first, operating the ball and switches with my feet was slow and difficult, but eventually using the controls got easier and I became faster.

I was happy to be working again! One thing worried me, though. How would my clients feel about this change? I was worried for nothing. Not only did they accept the change, but they were pleased to see me working again.

With the help of this technology, my work continued. Life went on, and I prepared for its next challenges.

When the Caregiver Needs Care

Cheryl and Sherry D'Attile in New Orleans, Louisiana, 2008.

Beginning in 1991, shortly after Ismail first started using the ventilator, he and I wrote and produced three educational videos that we felt would be helpful to families living with ALS and other debilitating illnesses. *What is ALS?* was a 15-minute educational video narrated by the actor Michael Gross for the National Amyotrophic Lateral Sclerosis Association. *It's Your Choice* was a 26-minute educational video to assist families who were making the decision about whether to use long-term mechanical respiratory support. *Caring for the*

Caregiver was a 28-minute educational video for caregivers. Ismail and I developed a facilitator's guide and workbook for an eight-hour interactive training program for caregivers to accompany our video.

The most important piece of advice we gave to caregivers was "Take care of yourself first." Easier said than done. Caregivers tend to get so caught up in taking care of their friend or loved one that their own wellbeing becomes a secondary concern—or no concern at all! One professional we interviewed reminded caregivers that flight attendants instruct passengers who are traveling with a child on an airplane to put on their own oxygen mask first in the event of cabin pressure change, then place the mask on their child. The reason is simple: you can't adequately take care of someone else unless you take care of yourself first. If you're not okay, the care of your loved one will suffer.

Caregivers are often vulnerable to illness because of the added physical and mental stress in their lives. If they are not healthy and strong, they may lack the stamina they need to take good care of their loved ones, and they could potentially infect them with communicable illnesses. Problems tend to become magnified in caregivers' minds when they're not feeling well. They run the risk of burnout.

"Take care of yourself first." Did I follow my own advice all the time? I knew what I was supposed to do. I knew how to do what I was supposed to do. I knew how important it was to do what I was supposed to do. I wanted to do what I was supposed to do. But sometimes I got so caught up in making sure Ismail's needs were met and that my full-time job responsibilities were accomplished, taking care of my own needs temporarily got pushed aside.

I'll Do It!

When nurses first started coming to our home to care for Ismail, I didn't know how to act. I felt guilty sitting around letting a nurse do all the work. I was Ismail's primary

NAME: _____

TEAM: _____

Kaiser Permanente	Ability Center	Chapter Booth/ Social Media *take your picture at the banner!
Quantum	Superior Mobility	Apguard Medical
AAA T.L.C. Healthcare	Cedars-Sinai	Boogie Board

Your 2016 LA Walk Day Passport

Use this passport to get all nine (9) stamps by visiting our eight (8) sponsors, Chapter booth and our Social Media Volunteer to post a walk day "shout out" to your Facebook or Twitter—tagging **@alsagoldenwest** AND **#NeverGiveUp #WalkToDefeatALS**

Turn your passport in at the **<u>Chapter booth by 12 PM (noon)</u>** for a chance to win. Drawing at 12:10PM—***must be present to win*** caregiver. I knew how to do his care. I didn't want the nurse to think I was lazy. So I would jump up and start assisting with the care. Some nurses thought this was great. Others kept reminding me that this was supposed to be my respite time. They encouraged me to go out somewhere or take a nap so that I would be ready to take over Ismail's care when I was alone with him overnight. It took a while, but eventually I began to get it. The nurses are licensed and trained and are being paid to take care of Ismail. They are there so I can rest or get to my job or take care of the millions of other things I need to do. They are there so I won't burn out. I have my own eight-hour shift to do every night. I don't need to do their shifts, too.

Preparing For My Golden Years

The first few months after I retired from my full-time corporate job in July, 2012, I spent a lot of time in doctors' offices, addressing medical issues I had ignored for a long time. In fact, it seemed as if I was spending most of my time in medical clinics. This was not how I wanted to spend my time in retirement! But I was able to get a number of pesky medical issues resolved.

Battle of the Bulge

I've battled a weight problem all of my life. When I get stressed, I turn to food. When I get angry or anxious or bored or happy or excited or sad, I turn to food. Ismail has learned this about me. Whenever I get upset at something and begin to rant and rave, he calmly spells out to me "Go eat." That always makes me laugh. I have to admit that when I take his advice, I feel better afterwards. I know that's not the right way to handle stress.

Someone once told me "whenever you feel stressed or angry or bored, go out and run around the block or play a game of tennis." Right. At eleven o'clock at night? Eating is so much easier. And the rewards are immediate. Programs like Weight Watchers teach you better ways to handle stress and all those other things that can derail healthy living. I once lost nearly 70 pounds on Weight Watchers, achieved my ideal weight, and became a lifetime member. I maintained my ideal weight for three years. Then a stressful period of my life got me off track. Unfortunately, once I get off-track it takes me a long time — sometimes years — to get back on a healthy program.

I can see the progression of my weight gain in the Ismail's Supporters' ALS Walk team pictures we take every year. The first year we participated in the walk, I was at my ideal weight. I looked good! By the next year, I was a little heavier. The following year, heavier still. At the last couple of walks, an extra large team shirt was beginning to look snug, and I was doing my best to hide myself behind Ismail's wheelchair.

Determined to take better care of myself and to get back down to a healthy weight, I recently returned to Weight Watchers and faced the scale. I have a long road back to my ideal weight, but I'm taking it one day, one pound, at a time. I've also returned to Jazzercise, where I'm doing aerobics dance three to four times a week. I feel good that I'm now taking better care of myself.

Happy Feet

With a million things to worry about, the last thing on my "to worry about" list was my feet, but mine were beginning to hurt all the time. I ignored the pain and hobbled around for a long time. When the pain got to the point that the only shoes I could wear were a pair of old broken down loafers, I decided it was time to give my feet some attention. Why couldn't I have Ismail's feet? They're beautiful and smooth! I'd gladly trade him my veins. My veins are big and full of free-flowing blood. His are tiny, hard to find, and stingy with their blood. Getting blood tests are a painful ordeal for both Ismail and the phlebotomist.   And intravenous therapies?   Torturous. Unfortunately, I can't give Ismail my veins, and I can't have his feet. I'm stuck with my own feet. I had to do something about them.

A friend recommended a local day spa, where I could not only get a good pedicure but also have the full spa treatment: a robe, a dark and quiet relaxation room, soothing spa music, an eye pillow to block out the light so I could nap during the treatment if I wanted, creams and lotions slathered all over my feet and legs, and a fabulous foot and leg massage. Sounded dreamy. I decided to treat myself. Yes, it was expensive, but it felt so good! I've been treating myself to the pedicure and spa treatment every two weeks ever since.   It's the one extravagant gift I give to myself to help reduce stress and keep my feet in good condition. I look forward to that hour of pampering twice a month. And I can walk again! I can even jump around during Jazzercise!

When I Need to Get Away

Ever since we met, Ismail and I had been inseparable. We went everywhere together, did everything together. We often worked together, traveled together, went to dinner and movies together. We never had an interest in taking separate vacations or having a boy's night out, or a girl's night out for that matter.   Then our lives changed and it was no longer possible to do everything together. It took me a long time before I felt comfortable going out without Ismail. I felt guilty. And resentful.   I wanted to share everything with my husband, as I had always done. Going to a movie alone, or even with a friend, just wasn't the same as going out on a movie date with the man I love. And how could I go to a party and leave Ismail at home? It didn't seem right.

I turned down many invitations because I didn't want to attend an event without him. In 1990, I declined an invitation to a newspaper awards dinner, where I was one of the feature writers to be presented with a first place award for business reporting by the Associated Press News Executives Council of

California and Nevada. The newspaper I had worked for invited me to attend the dinner, but the invitation did not include Ismail. Although I was grateful for the invitation and proud of the award, I wouldn't leave Ismail home alone.

As time went on I began to realize if I didn't start doing things on my own from time to time, I would be venturing out of the house less and less. The trips I did take would consist mainly of going back and forth to work and to Ismail's medical appointments. The years would slip away, and I would miss out on many of life's opportunities. Neither Ismail nor I wanted that. Fortunately, we continue to share fun outings together. I cherish those times.

Often Ismail prefers to let me do the socializing for the two of us and stay home to enjoy the comfort of his 80-degree family room, his big-screen television, and his well-regulated daily routine. At home, he doesn't have to worry about working out the logistics of getting his wheelchair up the stairs of someone's house, avoiding sunken living rooms, or shivering in someone else's 70-degree home. And he doesn't have to deal with personal care issues, like finding a private place where he can be suctioned or reclined in his wheelchair to use the urinal.

Venturing Out Alone

Besides working full-time, which I continued to do until my 2012 retirement, I got myself out of the house for short "breaks" in a number of ways. I learned to go out occasionally by myself or with friends, and I sometimes went to dinner, movies, and museums alone. Some people find it depressing to be alone. I'm glad I'm the kind of person who finds peace and serenity in being by myself from time-to-time. Whenever I'm stressed, angry, or upset, spending a day by myself at a museum or sitting alone in a movie theatre with a box of popcorn and a diet soda does wonders to calm my nerves and get my mind off of my challenges and into some fun, fascinating, or adventurous place.

Several years passed by before I would consider going on an overnight trip away from home, even though Ismail now had nursing care and I could arrange for temporary 24-hour care for him if I needed it. My job once required me to conduct two days of training sessions in San Diego, California. Although the company offered to pay for a hotel room, I opted to drive 160 miles home so I could be with Ismail overnight and then drive back another 160 miles to San Diego early the following morning.

A few years later, my job required me to stay overnight in Oakland, California from time to time. The 370 miles between home and Oakland was an impractical distance to drive twice a day and somehow make it on time to 8:00 a.m. meetings. So, I had to adjust to arranging overnight nursing care for Ismail and spending occasional nights in Oakland. I usually stayed at Jack London Square, a charming place on the waterfront that houses fine restaurants, stores, a movie theatre, a large bookstore, as well as a cabin that Jack London once lived in. The cabin had been re-located from the Klondike region of the Yukon. This had special meaning to me because Jack London is one of Ismail's favorite writers. I liked to stay at a hotel on the waterfront that had many rooms with beautiful views of the water. Although these occasional overnight trips to Oakland were work-related, I began to enjoy them as opportunities for mini-respites.

Planning Short Vacations

My first multi-night trip away from home was a weekend visit with my brother, Ron, and sister-in-law, Sarah, in Atlanta, Georgia in the late 1990s. It had been several years since I had seen them, and they were encouraging me to come for a visit. Although I would have loved for Ismail to have been able to come along, it would have been nearly impossible to organize all the complicated arrangements necessary to make such a trip happen, including getting him and his ventilator on an airplane, convincing one of his nurses to leave her family and come with us to Atlanta, and figuring out a way to get medical equipment and supplies across the country and into my relatives' home. Besides, I have to admit that after several years of caregiving, I needed a break.

Planning for trips is always complicated. I first have to arrange for 24-hour care for Ismail and ensure there are no holes in the schedule for the entire time I plan to be away. This can be a daunting feat, especially if there aren't enough backup nurses working on the case to cover all of the overnight shifts. Only high-quality ventilator-trained nurses familiar with Ismail and his special needs are allowed to work for us. Fortunately, we currently have a great staff of ventilator-trained nurses of the highest quality, most of whom have been caring for Ismail for many years and are flexible in taking on extra hours or rearranging their schedules to accommodate our needs.

Before I leave on any trip, I also need to order medications Ismail will need while I'm away and check to be sure he has enough food and supplies. I might have to make a new batch of soup to store in the freezer to be sure Ismail will have enough for dinner every night while I'm gone.

When Things Don't Go as Planned

That first trip I made to Atlanta was especially complicated and stressful. I had conflicting feelings about going away. I looked forward to having a weekend break. I was happy about seeing my relatives. I also felt guilty. Anxious. What if something happened to Ismail while I was on the other side of the country? Everyone, including Ismail, encouraged me to go. His nurses assured me they would take good care of him and that he'd be all right. If anything happened, I was only a phone call away. I could hop on a plane and be home in a matter of hours. Hours. That's a long time if something was wrong. They promised nothing would happen. I meticulously attended to all the details of preparing to leave and had everything in order—except for one thing, one little thing: the agency hadn't been able to fill the first overnight shift for the initial day of my trip. If they couldn't find a nurse to cover that shift, I wasn't going anywhere.

I was up all night before I left making phone calls to the nursing agency and to the airport shuttle. The shuttle was scheduled to pick me up early in the morning. I had until an hour prior to their pick-up time to cancel. And I didn't know until an hour or so prior to pick-up whether I was actually going to be able to make the trip. Then, the agency called. They had a nurse to send. A nurse we had never met. She had experience taking care of other ventilator patients, they said. It was her or nobody. I didn't have a good feeling about this. I asked Ismail whether I should cancel my trip. Of course, he said, "no." I got on the shuttle and onto the plane. I worried all the way to Atlanta.

The nurse who worked the day I left stayed late so that she could give the new nurse an orientation. It made me feel better knowing that a nurse I knew and trusted would be training the new nurse, who would be caring for Ismail overnight. Hopefully, he'll fall asleep and the night will be peaceful and uneventful. There won't be much for her to do while he's asleep. Maybe suction him a couple of times. Hopefully the ventilator won't malfunction. Hopefully, he won't become disconnected. What if he becomes disconnected! What if something goes wrong with the ventilator! Deep breaths. The nurse has experience with ventilators. Everything should be fine. Should be.

The minute I disembarked from the plane at the Atlanta airport, Ron and Sarah ran over to greet me. I gave them each a quick hug and kiss and asked them to wait for me while I rushed over to the pay phones to call home. Ismail's regular nurse answered the phone. She was in the middle of orienting the new nurse. She sounded stressed. My stomach knotted. This was not good. "Everything's all right," the nurse said, her voice tight, unconvincing. Should I catch the next flight home? Ron and Sarah watched me with concern from a few feet away, wondering what was going on, why I looked so stressed.

Things went from bad to worse. One of our other regular nurses had a family emergency and had to cancel all of her shifts that week. I was on the phone practically every hour calling home all weekend long. Had they found someone to do the shifts? Had they tried calling this nurse? That nurse? Could they rearrange people's shifts to fill in the holes in the schedule? I was about to make arrangements to fly back home, when the agency finally got the empty shifts covered. I was able to stay in Atlanta after all and enjoy the short time remaining with Ron and Sarah, who went out of their way to be comforting and reassuring and to make me feel at home and relaxed. Despite their best efforts, what was meant to be a short vacation for me, a time to enjoy a visit with my family and get a little rest and relaxation, turned out to be more stressful than if I had just stayed home.

When I did get back home, I learned the truth about what really happened that first night of my trip. I had every reason to worry, the nurse who did that first night's orientation admitted. The nurse the agency had sent for the overnight shift was "strange," our nurse told me. She had a lot of trouble getting her to understand anything, and she was so worried about Ismail being left in her care that she hated to leave that night. She called first thing the following morning to make sure Ismail was still alive. Ismail told me that every time the nurse touched his ventilator, he became disconnected. It was a scary experience for him. Finally, he told her not to touch the ventilator again, hoping he'd get through the rest of the night without any equipment problems. I also learned from our next- door neighbor that the nurse woke him in the middle of the night, terrified that someone was in the house. Our neighbor, who had let us provide his name and phone number in case of an emergency, put on his clothes and came over to check things out. He looked in every room, every closet, and found no traces of an intruder. Whatever the nurse had heard or imagined she heard spooked her all night. The nurse coming on duty the following morning found her curled up under the desk in my home office, where she had cowered all night.

Better Times; Better Trips

I've taken many out-of-town trips since then, and I've made certain that we've never had to experience another incident like that. I'm happy to say that we never have. I've made several trips now to Georgia, and to New Orleans with Ron and Sarah and once with my dear friend and traveling companion, Sherry. With Sherry, whom I've known since junior high school and is like a sister to me, I've taken short vacations to Catalina Island and to Vancouver, Canada. Sherry and I have also gone to Las Vegas more than once, and to Boston, New England, and Washington, D.C. In May, 2013, we went to London for a week. London was a special trip for us because it was the first time we had returned together to that beautiful, elegant, exciting city since we lived and worked there when we were 18-year-old first-year college students. During all of these trips, I've felt comfortable with the nurses who would be caring for Ismail during my absence and confident that they could handle any emergency. I've had backup nurses on stand-by in case of cancellations.

Many thanks to Sherry for being a dear friend and fun traveling companion. And special thanks to our dedicated nurses, who take great care of Ismail and ensure that I never have to worry about his safety when I'm out of town.

Summer Fun

Cheryl and Ismail at Ventura Harbor, Ventura, CA, August 2014

I love summer. I welcome its sun and hot temperatures, and I love to sunbathe on my patio with my feet propped up on a chair, a baseball cap shading my face, and my shirt off so I can get a tan. The hotter the day the better!

Since I stay inside my warm house most of the winter, I like to go to fun places when I can on warm summer days. I recently went to the Los Angeles Zoo and enjoyed watching an elephant training demonstration and seeing all the other beautiful animals. I usually visit Fisherman's Wharf at the Harbor in Ventura, California once a year. There are nice shops and restaurants at the harbor, and I like to take Cheryl and my nurses to lunch at a restaurant called The Greek that overlooks the water and the boats. Cheryl always buys a couple of extra orders of Moussaka to bring home for my dinner. Moussaka is a delicious Greek casserole made with layers of eggplant (or potatoes), ground meat, and a tomato-based sauce, then topped with a cream sauce. This restaurant uses eggplant. There are Greek singers and belly dancers at the restaurant on weekend nights. Several years ago, Cheryl and I and one of our nurses went to The Greek for one of our wedding anniversary celebration dinners. We enjoyed watching the Greek singers and dancers. My nurse tucked dollar bills in my headband for the belly dancers to come and take as they danced in front of me, giving me big smiles. That was fun!

One of my favorite vacation places is the beautiful village of La Jolla, California. Cheryl and I have gone there several times, both before and after I was diagnosed with ALS. La Jolla Cove is located at the edge of the Pacific Ocean. It has beautiful views. The small beach at the cove is located beside a street that runs in front of many motels with windows that overlook the water. Waves splash against rocky cliffs below. The shops, restaurants, and coffee shops in the village are charming. Cheryl and I once had dinner at a small French restaurant that served fancy French food and had violinists roaming around playing romantic music. Cheryl says she had the best dinner of her life that night: abalone cordon bleu. The next time we went to La Jolla, all Cheryl talked about was going to that restaurant again and ordering the same dish. We walked up and down the streets of the village, but could never find the restaurant again.

Big Splash

La Jolla is a short drive away from San Diego, where you can spend a day at the San Diego Zoo or at my favorite theme park, Sea World.

I used to love watching the Sparkletts Water Fantasy Show at Sea World. I was fascinated with the different colored lights mixed with water. The colorful dancing water was pleasing to my eyes and soul. Unfortunately, that show is no longer in existence. It has been replaced by other shows.

I like the dolphins, the penguins, and the other animals at Sea World, but my favorites are the killer whales that perform in Shamu Stadium. They are amazing. One time, when Cheryl, a nurse and I arrived to see the show, I was feeling uncomfortable because traveling in my van and being driven around in my wheelchair causes my body to slide down in my chair. That creates pain in my bottom and my back. To correct this, I have to be reclined flat in my wheelchair and pulled up by my hips so I can sit up straight in my wheelchair once again. Reclining me in my chair and pulling me up also serves as a pressure release that helps to prevent pressure sores.

While we were waiting for the whale show to begin, I asked my nurse to pull me up in my wheelchair. I suggested a space that looked large enough for reclining the chair and repositioning me. It was in front of the audience, next to the whales' pool. Cheryl said she would stand in front of me and the nurse to try to partially block the view of the audience so I could have some privacy. Unfortunately, the show started before the nurse was able to complete pulling me up. Loud music started, and in a minute, whales were swimming around and leaping in the water next to us on the other side of the rail. A whale leapt up right next to us and splashed back into the water with tremendous force, spraying water all over us and others in the "splash zone." The three of us were soaked, but I was very lucky. My ventilator did not get too wet!

I have heard that Sea World has added many new shows and exhibits since the last time I was there. Maybe I'll go back to see them! Next time I'll stay out of the "splash zone."

A Day at the Huntington

There are many interesting places to visit in Pasadena, California. My favorite is the Huntington Library, Art Collections, and Botanical Gardens. There is so much to see there.

In the library, I like to look at the rare books and manuscripts. There's a Gutenberg Bible and a special collection of early editions of Shakespeare's works.

All of the gardens at the Huntington are beautiful. Some have sculptures displayed on their lawns. The Rose Garden is bright, colorful and lush. It always cheers me up to see its big, beautiful flowers. Sometimes Cheryl and my nurse have lunch in the little Rose Garden tea room, where we can see the roses through the picture windows. In the Japanese and Chinese Gardens, we love to look at the koi-filled ponds, rocks, bridges, ornate Japanese and Chinese buildings, and lush oriental landscape.

Inside the art gallery are the paintings of some of the greatest masters of the world of art. Two of the most famous paintings on display are Blue Boy by Thomas Gainsborough and Pinkie by Thomas Lawrence. They are my two favorite paintings in the collection. Cheryl and I always make sure to see them and many other beautiful 18th and 19th century British paintings every time we go to the Huntington.

One day many years ago, Cheryl and I and one of my nurses were enjoying the paintings in the art gallery. We stopped to view them one-by-one, admiring the rich colors, realistic detail, and the contrast of light and shadow of Blue Boy and Pinkie.

I looked to my side and saw a little girl smiling at me. Just as I was fascinated by the paintings, she was fascinated by my wheelchair and respiratory equipment. I was still able to talk at that time and asked her how old she was. "Four," she replied. When I asked her name, she ran to her parents. As Cheryl and I continued to view the paintings, the little girl followed us wherever we went, watching me and smiling at me. I enjoyed having this new little friend. We finished viewing the paintings and headed for the door to go out to enjoy the gardens. As we started to leave, we heard the little girl crying. We stopped to wave good-bye to her, but we lost her and her parents in the large crowd of people in the room. I felt sad that we could not say goodbye to my special friend.

Outside, we viewed the gardens and smelled the perfume of the flowers. After a while, I started to cough. I needed to be suctioned. To suction me, my nurse has to temporarily disconnect me from my ventilator and insert a long, thin catheter down my trachea, then use a machine to gently suction out mucous. Suctioning is not a pleasant thing to watch, but it is necessary for my health. I did not want to be suctioned in front of the other visitors, so we looked for a private spot. When we found a secluded area, my nurse started to suction me, while Cheryl stood in front so others would not notice. In a few seconds, however, people started to come over to watch, and soon a large crowd surrounded us. The crowd began to get very close. My nurse asked them to give us some space and privacy, but the crowd did not move or respond. The nurse got agitated, but I told her not to worry. Looking at the crowd, I said to the nurse in as loud a voice I could, "I only charge five dollars per person for each show." Within a few moments, the crowd disappeared.

When the nurse finished suctioning me, we continued viewing the gardens and enjoying the day. The lush green lawns and bushes, the tall trees, the fresh, cool water, and the vibrant flowers were all reminders of the preciousness of life. After a while, we headed home after enjoying another wonderful day at the Huntington.

Seaside Arts and Crafts

The beautiful city of Santa Barbara is located a little over an hour's drive from our home. Besides the city itself, there are many attractions to visit and enjoy. At the edge of the city is Stearns Wharf, covered with restaurants, shops, and many other interesting things to visit, including a fish market.

For Cheryl and me, the main attraction is the arts and crafts by local artists that are displayed every Sunday along a grassy area beside Carrillo Boulevard, next to the Pacific Ocean. There are hundreds of original drawings, paintings, graphics, sculpture, photographs, hand-made jewelry, woodwork, candles, and other crafts. Over 30 years ago, we bought a wood spice cabinet for our kitchen wall. It still looks beautiful in our kitchen today and reminds us of happy times we spent in Santa Barbara before I had ALS.

On one visit to Santa Barbara after I started using a ventilator, my nurse drove my power wheelchair slowly along Carrillo Boulevard, while Cheryl walked beside us. We went from display to display, looking at all of the interesting art work. The artists were eager to talk to us and show us their work. Cheryl and I purchased two beautiful paintings from Eugene Schmidt who was born in Germany in 1919 and had been painting in Santa Barbara for 32 years. He shared with us a letter on Buckingham Palace stationary that thanked him on behalf of Queen Elizabeth II of England for two "charming paintings" of the Old Spanish Mission and the Courthouse at Santa Barbara.

The artist held our paintings for us until we went home so we wouldn't have to carry them around with us the rest of the day.

We looked around at more paintings. When we were tired and hungry, we headed for a restaurant we liked on the wharf. Going down the wharf to the restaurant was rough for me. My wheelchair had no shock absorbers! I bumped all the way to the restaurant! My whole body was bouncing around. I felt like my brains were jumping around inside my head. I couldn't wait to get to the restaurant, but it felt like it was a hundred miles away! By the time we got there, my body had slipped down in my wheelchair, and I had to be pulled back up. My nurse reclined me outside the restaurant and pulled me up higher in my chair. People looked at us funny. I didn't care. I was comfortable again.

Inside the restaurant, the hostess sat us at a table by a window, where we could see part of the city and part of the beach. After a few minutes, a waitress came over and gave each of us a menu. Cheryl and my nurse ordered fish. I was still able to eat by mouth at that time, but I was having trouble chewing and swallowing, so I ordered a bowl of clam chowder. By now, control of my arms and hands had left me. Since I could not use them anymore, Cheryl had to feed me. Between each bite of her food, she gave me a spoonful of soup. The soup was very tasty, and Cheryl and I enjoyed sharing our lunch together.

When we finished eating, Cheryl paid the bill, and we headed back to the arts and crafts. I looked down the wharf and dreaded the ride back. The art exhibits looked so far away. What could I do? I bounced along the bumpy wharf all the way back, wondering if I could get shock absorbers put on my wheelchair!

After we got back to the exhibits and I was pulled back up in my wheelchair, we looked at more displays of handmade items, such as leather coats and handbags, leather belts, wooden shelves, cabinets, and jewelry. When we finished browsing through the crafts, we picked up the paintings we had bought and headed back to our van.

Even though I got bounced around on the wharf, I loved our visit to Santa Barbara. What a beautiful day that had been!

Perilous Times

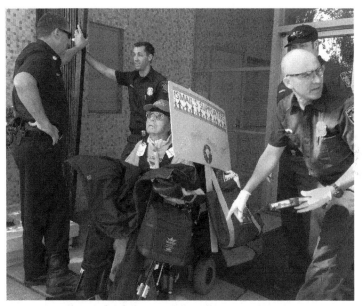

Ismail with firefighters and paramedics after the
Los Angeles County Walk to Defeat ALS event in October 2014

When your husband is on life support and is unable to fend for himself, you've got to be prepared for emergencies. Any emergency. At any time. We have three doors in our home that we could use as escape routes (the front door, the sliding glass door that leads to the patio in the back, and another sliding glass door that leads to the side of the house). We have an elaborate emergency plan in place involving a Lifeline Medical Alert system that is monitored 24 hours a day, seven days a week. We have provided the medical alert company with a list of neighbors for it to call, along with 911, in the event of an emergency. I have instructed each of these neighbors on what to do if they receive a call. Should Ismail and I ever have any type of emergency, our medical alert company and neighbors will take action.

Of course, no matter how well I and Ismail's nurses plan for emergencies, life will always be full of surprises.

Whenever we go anywhere, even to a doctor's appointment, we take everything that we can imagine we would possibly need. Packed into his gigantic, bulging backpack-on-wheels are extra ventilator circuits and valves, extra suction catheters, an extra trach tube, feeding syringes, a can of Glucerna, a bottle of water, a plastic urinal, gloves, nitroglycerine, an extra set of keys to the house and van, and many other essential items. Of course, we never leave the house without the ambu bag, a manual device that we can use to inflate Ismail's lungs with air in the event something happens to his ventilator, and a portable suction machine. We hang both of these items on the wheelchair handles by the straps of their cases. We carry in the van an extra battery for his ventilator, too. Just in case. Sometimes, that still isn't enough.

Stranded in Exposition Park

On October 19, 2014, we participated in the ALS Association's Walk to Defeat ALS at Exposition Park in Los Angeles. As soon as we arrived at the event and parked the van, the external battery on Ismail's ventilator went dead. I couldn't believe it. It was a brand new battery and had been fully charged the night before. Thank goodness we brought an extra battery. I got it out from the back of the van. We connected it to the ventilator, and off we went to the walk.

It was an excellent event, and we had a wonderful time. As our team enjoyed a picnic lunch after the walk, I noticed that our nurse and a few of our team members were gathered around Ismail several feet away connecting his ventilator to a very long cable stretching from the bandstand. "The external battery is dead," the nurse informed me as I walked over. How could that be? It was also a new fully-charged battery that had been running only about 3 ½ hours. It should have lasted 6-8 hours.

We were 40 miles from home. It would take at least an hour to drive home, longer if we ran into traffic. The ventilator's internal battery would last about 30 to 45 minutes. "We'll never get him home," I said. My mind was racing, frantically searching for a solution. "There's no way we can get him home."

The event was over and the sound engineers were packing up their equipment. They needed their cable. Now what? A couple of our team members found an electrical outlet outside one of the museums. We plugged Ismail's ventilator into it and set up camp.

I called the emergency line for our DME company and told them we needed a fully charged external battery delivered to us as soon as possible. It was Sunday afternoon. Not the ideal time for a ventilator emergency. It took several calls to the company's emergency line before I was finally able to speak to the respiratory therapist on call. She told me she wasn't sure she could find a charged battery in the warehouse and, if she could, didn't know how long it would take her to get it to us. "We don't have any choice but to wait for you to get here," I told her, "and we need you to get here as soon as possible."

Several of our wonderful friends stayed with us, providing emotional support and helping us brainstorm. They refused to leave until they were assured we would get home okay. Some members of the ALS Association staff stayed with us, too, offering ideas and providing their support.

We considered trying to arrange for medical transportation home, but I was afraid that option would cost thousands of dollars that we might have to pay for out-of-pocket. I called 911. The paramedics would probably transport Ismail to the nearest hospital. At least he would be safe. We could wait there for the respiratory therapist to meet us with a new battery. Besides, the fire department might have some kind of battery charger on their truck that we could use.

Sirens blaring, two fire trucks and a paramedics truck pulled up a few minutes later. Friendly, helpful firefighters and paramedics assessed the situation. Unfortunately, they didn't have a battery charger that would work for us. They hesitated taking Ismail to a hospital.

"We have to get him to a safe environment," our nurse told the fire captain.

"He is in a safe environment," the captain said. "He's comfortable. His ventilator is plugged in to an electrical outlet and working properly. As long as he remains plugged in and his ventilator is getting electricity, he's fine."

"If we take him to a hospital, he can be exposed to potential infections," someone else on the rescue team explained. "The hospital will admit him and transfer him to one of its own ventilators."

I knew that hospital ventilators do not function well with Ismail's uncuffed tracheostomy tube. There would be the trauma of the transport, transferring Ismail from his power chair onto a gurney, bagging him with an ambu bag until he could be connected to another ventilator.

Since we didn't know when or if the respiratory therapist would be able to bring us a charged battery, the Fire Captain suggested that I call a neighbor or friend to go to our home to pick up a couple of additional charged batteries we had in the house and bring them to us. That would be twice as fast as my driving all the way home and then back again (at least a 2-hour round trip). My brother Jim and sister-in-law Lynn live very close to our home. I hated to ask them to make that long drive, but they graciously agreed to help. Fortunately, they didn't have to. The respiratory therapist showed up with a battery before Jim and Lynn got to our house. We connected the battery to Ismail's ventilator. It was charged, the ventilator worked, and we were finally on our way home!

Carmel

Carmel is one of Ismail's very favorite places, and we have been there many times. We have had wonderful experiences there, enjoying the mountains and the panoramic ocean views, wandering around its quaint village of shops and restaurants and fine art galleries. On one occasion several years ago, however, when one of our nurses and I took Ismail there for a special weekend get-away, we ran into an unexpected problem. Since Carmel is located more than 300 miles from our home, we double-checked before we left the house to make sure we had everything with us we could possibly need. Everything. Including a portable microwave and a hand blender with which to prepare Ismail's meals. After all, we couldn't run back home to pick up something we forgot.

I had been driving over five hours when we arrived at Carmel in the early evening. We checked into our motel and, once in the room, positioned Ismail next to an electric outlet so we could charge his electric wheelchair and his ventilator. To my surprise, I couldn't insert the ventilator's plug into the electrical socket. The plug had three prongs. The outlet accommodated only two prongs. There must be a three-pronged outlet somewhere in the room I reasoned. I found another outlet. It, too, only accommodated plugs with two prongs. I kept searching, beginning to become alarmed. No three-prong outlets in the entire room. Panic swept over me. Ismail's ventilator had been unplugged all day while we traveled. The external battery would soon be drained, and the internal battery would last an hour or less. We didn't have an adapter with us. It's not that we forgot to pack it. We didn't own one! Of all the things in the world I imagined we might need on this, or any trip within the United States, it was an adapter to allow us to plug in a three-prong plug! How old was this motel anyway?

I ran to the motel's front desk and explained our problem to the clerk. Did he know where I could buy an adapter? No. Not at this time on a Friday night. Carmel is a very small town. All of the local shops would be closed. I frantically explained our situation. Ventilator. Life support. Battery about to go out. A kind man, the clerk rummaged through drawers. He pulled out an adapter and handed it to me. I clenched it gratefully. At that moment, it was the most beautiful thing in the world, and the clerk was our hero. He saved Ismail's life! Well, at least, a possible trip to the local emergency room!

I hurried back to our room and connected the adapter to the plug on Ismail's ventilator, then inserted the plug into the wall outlet. It slipped right in, and the ventilator's battery began to recharge. I let out a big cheer. Saved!

Guess what we now carry in Ismail's backback and take everywhere we go? We'll probably never need that adapter again, but we've got it with us now — just in case!

Earthquake

It shook me awake. Violently. Its rumble tore through the darkness. Terror gripped me.

I'm a native Californian. I've lived in earthquake country all my life. Still, every time the rumbling starts and the shaking awakens me from a deep sleep, I wonder whether it's the end of the world. I'll never get used to earthquakes. No matter how many times I live through them. No matter how many earthquake drills I participate in. You can collect canned food and bottled water. You can carefully work out an emergency plan. But when an earthquake hits, you know how helpless you are in the face of an overpowering force of nature.

It was January 17, 1994. When I was awake enough to realize it was an earthquake shaking the room, I scrambled out of bed and staggered over to Ismail. His ventilator was screaming, warning me that the electricity in the house had gone out and that it was running off the power of an external back-up battery. Lamps, vases, dishes crashed onto the floor throughout the house. I heard the awful shattering of glass. It was 4:31 a.m. and the house was pitch black. I squinted through the darkness to see Ismail's face, to make sure he was all right. He seemed frightened, but okay. Miraculously, the ventilator stayed in its place on the dresser beside the bed, undamaged, determinedly pumping out breaths in a calm, metered rhythm, keeping Ismail alive. I held onto Ismail until the shaking stopped.

Then, I went back to bed. After all, it was now quiet and still, and Ismail and I were both all right. It was too dark to walk around the house anyway, and there was broken glass all over the floor. Might as well stay in bed until the morning grew lighter. Then, I'd get up and assess the damage to the house and decide what to do next. But a couple of minutes later, the doorbell rang.

It was our next door neighbor, Harry, checking in on us, making sure we were okay and asking if we needed anything. Bless our caring neighbors. It's comforting to know that if Ismail or I had been hurt, our neighbor would have been there within minutes to provide help. I assured him we were both okay and said I didn't think we needed anything, but that I would come and get him if we did. He assured me he'd check in on us from time to time.

Standing in my nightgown, holding a flashlight, I saw that the floor was littered with stuff that had fallen off of shelves and walls and shattered on the floor. Among broken mementos, I discovered a miracle. The Swiss cuckoo clock Ismail loved was still hanging on the wall, undamaged. Its cheerful bird continued to announce the time as its wooden dancers twirled to happy music every hour.

Then came the curve ball. Lined up on the sink were a half dozen empty plastic bottles that had once been filled with the boiled water we use to suction Ismail. Once a bottle is empty, we sterilize it and refill it with water we have boiled for ten minutes. In those days we scheduled one day a week to boil water for Ismail's suctioning. This was the day that was supposed to happen. But it wasn't going to happen today. We had no working stove. Ismail would certainly need to be suctioned. There was only one bottle of boiled water left on the shelf. We would run out before the end of the day.

The doorbell rang again. It was my brother, Jim, whose own house unfortunately sustained more damage than ours. After making sure his family was okay, he made the treacherous trek across Simi Valley, through dark, damaged streets with no operating traffic signals, to make sure we were okay. He told me the freeway to and from the San Fernando Valley had been badly damaged and was closed. A feeling of isolation closed in. There were only two routes in and out of Simi Valley, and we had just lost one of them, perhaps for months. It was the freeway most people used to get in and out of our valley. It was the one I used to get to and from work.

A couple of hours after my brother left, the doorbell rang yet again. I opened the door to find one of our nurses standing on the porch. "I can't believe you came! " I gasped, bursting into tears and throwing my arms around her. "Thank you so, so much! How did you get here?" She explained that she took surface streets all the way from the adjacent valley and drove through a mountain pass. I was stunned and grateful. What a heroine! Now that she was here to take care of Ismail, I could take his portable suction machine and back-up ventilator to the local hospital a few blocks away. The hospital would have electrical power provided by a generator. Hopefully, the staff would allow me to plug in the machines to recharge their batteries. Maybe, just maybe, they would sell me a bottle or two of normal saline to use for suctioning Ismail.

The hospital staff was fantastic. Welcoming. Reassuring. Helpful. They let me plug Ismail's ventilator and suction machine into their outlets to recharge them. When I asked about normal saline, they handed me several large bottles of it, declining to take any money in payment.

You never know how dependent you are upon the kindness of others until you are faced with a major emergency and find that your life or that of someone you love depends on help from your family, your friends, your neighbors, and people in the community. Thank God Ismail and I are surrounded by generous and loving people. We wouldn't be here today without them.

And that once-a-week water-boiling schedule of ours? We now boil water for Ismail's suctioning every day, refilling each bottle as soon as it becomes empty. We have a portable generator, too, just in case we need it someday.

Fire

The morning of October 25, 2003 I saw a cloud of smoke far in the distance when I left home to go shopping in neighboring Thousand Oaks. That looks like a mean fire, I thought. I wonder where it's located. Fillmore? Piru? Is it farther away than it looks? I hope so. By the time I headed back home a couple of hours later, the horizon ahead of me was black. Angry smoke spread across Simi Valley, leading, it appeared, straight to our house. The closer I got to home, the scarier the smoke looked. Swept by heavy wind, the fire had spread to the other side of the hills that surrounded our neighborhood.

"We should leave the house," I told Ismail, "while we still have time to get out." He blinked twice at me. No. "Ismail," I pleaded. "We can go into the San Fernando Valley, where we will be safe. If we wait too long, we may not be able to get out." Two blinks. Ismail had dug in. He wasn't about to leave his home. Had to stand guard. As if his strong will could redirect the fire. Get out of here, fire! You don't want to tangle with Ismail!

I went outside every five minutes, checking to see if the smoke looked any better. Maybe the wind would shift and blow the fire the other way. But the sky looked blacker, angrier, every time I looked. And every time I ran back inside and announced that we had to evacuate, Ismail refused to budge.

I called the fire emergency phone number several times, trying to get an update and a recommendation concerning evacuation. Each time I called, they simply told me,

"Evacuation is not mandatory at this time." But when I asked if it recommended, they told me it was our decision. I explained our situation, Ismail's condition, the problems we would have evacuating him. They assured me that if I needed help, I could simply call and they would provide transportation and assistance.

I began setting things by the front door so they'd be easy to grab if we needed to get out. Ismail's backpack on wheels, his ambu bag, portable suction machine, a back-up ventilator battery, a box of important papers.

It was about nine o'clock at night when we got a knock at the door. It was someone from the fire department, advising me that if we wanted to evacuate, we had to get out NOW. Otherwise, we had to lock all of our doors and windows and stay inside and wait it out until we were notified that it was safe to leave the house. By this time, Ismail was already in bed, undressed. The nurse was preparing him to go to sleep. "Get him up! Now!" I told the nurse, not even asking for Ismail's opinion. "The fire department says we have to evacuate now!"

While the nurse got Ismail's clothes back on him and started to transfer him back to his wheelchair, I assessed our options and the quickest, safest way to get Ismail out of the house and to a safe place. I went outside to talk to one of the firefighters and was faced with a fleet of fire trucks parked outside our house. "My husband is disabled," I explained to one of the firefighters. "It's going to take time to get him and his life support equipment out of the house. Do I have time to get him into our van, or should I call the emergency line for assistance?"

"I'm very sorry," the firefighter answered. "There has been a misunderstanding. There is no mandatory evacuation at this time. You don't need to leave yet, if you don't want to."

"Oh, we're going to leave now," I said with determination. "I just need to know if I have time to get my husband and his equipment into the van."

"You have plenty of time," he assured me.

When you're in an emergency, it's hard to recall all the details of the emergency plans you so meticulously developed in your logical state of mind. And you don't always have time to look them up. Instinct and fear take over. "Get out! Get out! Get out!" my mind kept screaming.

I grabbed ventilator circuits, tubing, connectors, valves, handfuls of suction catheters, dressings, bottles of sterilized water. I stuffed everything into garbage bags. I swept Ismail's medications and vitamins out of the cupboard and into another bag, threw mine into a separate one. I stuffed some of Ismail's pants, shirts, and stockings into another bag. Everything into garbage bags! No time to organize, fold, or pack! No time to worry about family photos or computers. Things needed for survival only! Get what you can, as much as you can, and get out! Get out! Get out! Almost forgot my own clothes. I stuffed a couple of days' worth into another bag. Our living room looked like a garbage dump, bloated trash bags piled high near the front door.

It was time to start hauling everything out to the van. I had no idea how I was going to fit all the bags inside. I heard the doorbell and thought it was the fire department, notifying us to get out of the house immediately. When I opened the door, I saw a young woman standing in the porch light, holding a small girl in her arms. The woman looked worried. "Are you okay?" I had no idea who she was. Probably a concerned neighbor, I thought. How nice of her to stop by. "Is Uncle Ismail all right?" she asked.

Hollen! Our niece! She was the last person I expected to see standing on our porch that night. That's why in my confused state, I failed to recognize her and her daughter Cayleigh. I gave them each big hugs. "How can we help?" Hollen asked.

While I started throwing trash bags into the van, Hollen called her dad, my brother Jim. She told him we were preparing to evacuate. After a minute, she handed the phone to me.

"Where are you going?" Jim asked me.

"I don't know," I admitted. "I'm just going to get out of Simi Valley. That's all I know. Once we're in Chatsworth or Northridge, I'll find a phone booth with a phone directory and start making calls to hotels to see what kind of reservation I can get."

"I'll make some calls for you," he said. "I'll get back to you in a few minutes."

He made reservations for us at a Marriott Hotel in Woodland Hills. We had a plan! Over the hill and down Topanga Canyon, across the San Fernando Valley to the hotel. Now if we can just get all these trash bags loaded into the van. Will there be room for Ismail?

Neighbors saw us loading up the van and began to gather.

"You've decided to leave."

"Yes. What about you?"

"No. We're going to stick it out."

"So are we," someone else chimed in.

Others nodded in agreement. It appeared we were the only ones who were heading out of Dodge.

"We'll keep an eye on your house," our next-door neighbor promised. We exchanged hugs.

While neighbors helped me finish loading bags into the van, Hollen and Cayleigh, still inside the house, rummaged through cupboards and closets, hunting for scrapbooks, high school yearbooks, souvenirs, albums, boxes of family photos, our wedding pictures. Things I had no time to worry about. Hollen filled her car with them and stayed behind when we left, to continue her treasure hunt. I urged her to stop searching and get out of the house. The night sky was red along the top ridge of the hills behind our cul de sac, and the air was thick with smoke.

Hollen assured me she would leave in a few minutes and would stay safe. She promised to stop by our hotel room later and bring Ismail's Hoyer lift, which we weren't able to fit inside the jam-packed van. I learned later that she took

Cayleigh home and then came back, attempting to water our roof until hot embers, blowing down from the hills, began to burn her face. Jim told me she cried bitterly because she couldn't get our non-working automated garage door open so that she could drive my car to a safe place. Ismail and I were deeply touched. Hollen has a gigantic heart of gold and immense courage. She was a true heroine that night.

When we pulled up to the hotel and got Ismail out of the van, a man brought over a large luggage cart. "Do you need help with your bags?" he asked.

"Yes, please."

In our room, we waited out the night. It was a long one. Surrounded by plastic trash bags, we wondered whether these would be the only belongings we'd have left in the world. Where would we go if our house burned down? We had ventilator equipment to be cleaned and hung to dry in a clean area. We needed a hospital bed. A large commode chair. A Hoyer lift. Our nurses come and go every day and need a place to sit and write notes. There are supervising nurses and respiratory therapists who visit frequently. Medical supplies are delivered several times a month. And we need a place to store all of those supplies.

Sometime in the middle of the night, we saw the announcement on the local news. Our neighborhood was now under mandatory evacuation. Our neighbors had five minutes to get out when the firefighters came knocking, we later learned. How could we have gotten Ismail out of there in five minutes? If the neighborhood is under mandatory evacuation, I thought, the houses are in grave danger. It was seriously looking like we might become homeless.

Jim called early the next day. "Your house is fine," he told me. "I went over there to check it out. The fire burned the hills, all the way down to the back wall of your yard, but it didn't touch your house."

I let out a huge sigh of relief and gratitude. "Thank God."

Raising Awareness and Money for ALS

Ismail's team at the Los Angeles County Walk to Defeat ALS, October 2009

The ALS Association has helped Cheryl and me a lot throughout the years. It has given both of us emotional support and helped us deal with problems at every stage of ALS. We have had excellent case managers who have been there for us whenever we had questions or needed assistance, and the association has loaned us equipment from their equipment loan pool.

Cheryl and I have partnered with the ALS Association in a number of ways throughout the years. We have helped provide information about ALS for families and worked to raise awareness and money for ALS services and research. The association sometimes refers people to us who have recently been diagnosed with ALS. Sometimes these people need advice on how to find caregivers. Other times they are trying to decide whether to use a ventilator and want to talk with someone who has experience using one. Cheryl and I have always been happy to share our experiences with people and talk to them about how I cope with having ALS and living on a ventilator.

We have been participating in the ALS Association's Walk to Defeat ALS since 2005. My walk team, *Ismail's Supporters*, was small that first year. One of my nurses joined us with her husband and baby, and a friend of Cheryl's came with her husband. Eventually more people joined us at future walks. The walks are important because all the walkers raise money for the ALS Association and increase awareness of the disease by walking around streets in a big group wearing bright-colored team shirts and carrying signs and banners. The walks are always fun. I get to see lots of our friends and members of our family, and I also get a chance to meet other people who are living with ALS.

I love to watch the children at these walks. They always have so much fun running around and enjoying the day in the sun. I'm happy when my grandniece, Lily, and grandnephew, Landon, join my team. They are cute and funny and always have a good time.

I have become good friends with a boy named Charlie. Cheryl used to work with Charlie's father, Ken. Charlie and his parents come to almost all of our walks. When I first met Charlie, he was a very young boy. He has now grown into a wonderful young man. I always love to see Charlie. He calls me his "buddy." He has a great smile and a giant heart. Once when he saw that I was cold, Charlie took off his Dodgers cap and put it on my head to help keep me warm. That meant a lot to me because Charlie really loves his Dodgers cap. Dealing with ALS is hard, but Charlie's advice is to "Have a bigger smile." His advice made me smile bigger and made the walk more enjoyable.

In 2013, my team had a Pizza Night Family Fundraiser. The restaurant made a donation to the ALS Association of 20% of the sales from our group during a four-hour time period. Our fundraiser was fun and successful. Almost everyone we know loves pizza, and the restaurant sold sandwiches and salads, too. Even a group of people from Cheryl's Jazzercise class came to our Pizza Night. It was great meeting them. Now I know who Cheryl hangs out with three to four nights a week! They are nice people and wonderful friends.

Other Opportunities to Support the ALS Association

The educational videos Cheryl and I produced between 1991 and 1993 to help families living with ALS were another opportunity for us to support the ALS Association. *What is ALS?*, our 15-minute educational video was co-produced with the National ALS Association. Every time someone mentioned the association when they placed an order for our other videos, *It's Your Choice* and *Caring for the Caregiver*, we made a donation to the ALS Association.

Awareness and Advocacy Award

On May 15, 2003, I was honored to receive the *2003 Vice President's ALS Awareness and Advocacy Award* from the ALS March of Faces. Kyle G. Hahn, President of ALS March of Faces, sent a letter to me along with a certificate. His letter stated:

> *It is our esteemed honor to present this certificate and award to you for your outstanding achievements in raising public awareness of Amyotrophic Lateral Sclerosis and efforts in advocating for this devastating illness.*
>
> *You were chosen to receive this award by a committee of your peers, not only in recognition of these feats, but that you have done so in spite of your own affliction with ALS. The ALS community is extremely grateful for your dedication and accomplishment.*

As per your request, the $500 Cash Award that accompanies this tribute has been donated to ALS Association Greater Los Angeles Chapter for patient equipment.

We would like to invite you to join our ALS Awareness project, the ALS March of Faces Banner. We have included information on submitting your photo to participate along with over 1600 PALS from around the world.

Congratulations on winning this award. Our sincere wishes for the best to you and your family and our prayers that you stay strong.

> *Sincerely yours,*
> *Kyle G. Hahn, PALS*
> *President*

In an article published May 25, 2003, in our local newspaper, the *Ventura County Star*, I said, "Getting this award means a lot to me because it is from my peers." I went on to explain, "The award gives me a chance to make people aware of this disease, which kills blindly. It also gives me the chance to communicate with other PALS so we can give hope to one another and face our difficult challenges every day."

Donations from This Book

By buying this book, you are helping Cheryl and me continue to raise money for the ALS Association. We are donating a portion of the proceeds from the sales of our book to the association.

ALS Advocacy

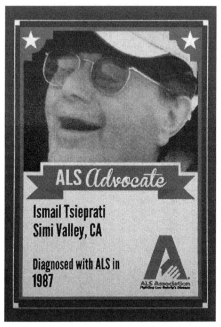

Ismail's ALS baseball card, May 2014

On March 28, 2014, Ismail received an email from the ALS Association about a unique Advocacy Day Opportunity. The email explains that in support of ALS Awareness Month and an upcoming Public Policy Conference in Washington, D.C. in May, the association was creating ALS Awareness Baseball Cards for individuals living with ALS to be presented to their congressional representative.

Ismail was invited to participate by sharing his story through the ALS Baseball Card awareness campaign. "Your active participation in the Walk to Defeat ALS raised invaluable awareness about ALS in your community," the email stated, "and contributed to research, care services, and advocacy initiatives at local, state, and federal levels.

The email went on to say that our congressperson needed to hear Ismail's voice on Capitol Hill and that this was an opportunity for Ismail to continue his efforts in building public awareness and generating ALS research funding by sharing his story with his congressional representative on one of the baseball cards.

Ismail was invited to submit a short sentence about his ALS story, a medium size high-resolution picture of himself, and two forms of contact that our Congressional representative could use to reach him. The email included an invitation for Ismail or a representative of his choice to register to attend the ALS Advocacy Day in Washington, D.C. and present his baseball card in person to our representative.

Since Ismail was not able to go to Washington, he appointed me as his representative. I was excited to join other ALS advocates from around the United States at the ALS Association's Annual Public Policy Conference May 7-9, 2014. It was great meeting people from other chapters in other parts of the country. About 100 of the advocates in attendance were people with ALS (PALS). I was able to talk to many of them, hear their stories, and share Ismail's story with them. I made new friends at the conference and look forward to keeping in touch with them.

As part of a delegation of five advocates from the ALS Association's Golden West Chapter, I went to Capitol Hill on May 8, National ALS Awareness Day, and met with representatives of eight members of congress. I shared with each of them the story of Ismail's battle with ALS and his determination to continue to live a happy and productive life. Explaining that Ismail's eye blink was beginning to grow weaker, I asked for their help. "We can't let ALS silence Ismail," I told them, "and we can't let it continue to kill so many people so quickly. We need increased funding for research projects that search for the cause and cure of ALS." Those who heard it were moved by Ismail's story of courage, determination, and optimism.

ALS advocates made four requests of congress:

1. Appropriate $10 million to continue and expand the functions of the National ALS Registry, which allows the association to collect data that may help determine what causes the disease and how it can be treated, prevented, and ultimately cured.

2. Appropriate $10 million to continue an ALS Research Program at the Department of Defense. This money would enable the funding of additional research projects to find new treatments for ALS for veterans, who have twice the risk of developing ALS than the general population, as well as for others living with the disease.

3. Enact the MODDERN Cures Act, which would accelerate the research for a treatment of ALS and other diseases by removing barriers that limit medical innovation and by providing incentives to develop new treatments and diagnostic tools.

4. Ensure access to Speech Generating Devices (SGDs) to people with ALS by stopping a new policy that changes the manner in which the Centers for Medicare and Medicaid Services (CMS) pays for these devices and, by doing so, limits the ability of people with ALS to access them.

Going to Capitol Hill was an exciting experience. It was fascinating to explore the intricate network of tunnels beneath the offices of our senators and representatives. We walked back and forth, from one end of the complex to the other, all day long, getting a worm's eye view of our nation's Capitol! I could barely walk by the end of the day, but I didn't mind.

Our advocacy work is making a difference. An ALS Association Advocacy Update distributed on September 12, 2014 announced that 200 senators and representatives have signed onto the SGD Dear Colleague letter that ALS advocates urged congress to support. The signed letter has been sent to the CMS Administrator.

Another victory for ALS advocates was Rep. Leonard Lance (R-NJ) reintroducing the MODDERN Cures Act in the House of Representatives. According to an ALS Association's Public Policy Action Alert, "the legislation provides new incentives to pursue ALS drug development and will significantly increase opportunities to find a treatment for the disease."

Participating in the ALS Association's Annual Public Policy Conference with other advocates on Capitol Hill to present Ismail's ALS story and request Congress's support for bills and issues important to the ALS community was a wonderful experience. I look forward to continuing my ALS advocacy and to future opportunities to make our voices heard.

The Power of Ice Buckets

Ismail, Cheryl, Jane and Phil do the "Ice Bucket Challenge" August 2014

When I was first told I had ALS, I didn't know what it was. When I told other people I had ALS, most of them didn't know what it was either. Even when Cheryl or I said it was "Lou Gehrig's Disease" a lot of people still didn't know what we were talking about. Some people had heard of the disease, but most didn't know very much about it. Then an amazing thing happened in the summer of 2014. The ALS Ice Bucket Challenge.

The Ice Bucket Challenge has been the greatest thing to ever happen to people with ALS. When I first heard about it, I never dreamed how big and important it was going to become. The idea is simple. It seems silly. Someone makes a videotape of themselves saying they are doing the Ice Bucket Challenge to raise awareness of ALS and money for ALS research and then dumps a bucket of ice water over their heads. They usually look really shocked and sometimes scream and jump around a few seconds because the water is so cold. Then they challenge some of their friends to do the same thing within 24 hours or donate $100 to ALS research. A lot of people donate the money because they don't want to dump ice water on their heads and post a video of themselves looking silly on the Internet. A lot of generous people have dumped the ice water and donated money too!

When we first heard about the Ice Bucket Challenge, Cheryl and I thought it would die out after a couple of weeks. We were wrong! More and more people started doing it. They challenged other people to do it. Ice bucket videos were all over Facebook. Television programs talked about it. Then they started doing it, too! Celebrities, politicians, and CEOs of big companies did it. They challenged other famous people to do it. People from around the world began doing it. Everybody was talking about ALS!

Cheryl and I did the Ice Bucket Challenge with our friends, Phil and Jane, who were visiting us for a couple of days from New York. They happened to be here at the right time to join us in the challenge. I wanted to participate, too, so I asked Cheryl to pour ice cubes over my head. My friends were surprised that I did that because everyone knows how cold I get, even when it's hot outside. Lucky for me, it was hot that day. Cheryl wanted to make sure everything went perfectly because she didn't want to have to do it twice. She made everybody practice first. After the practice, my nurse, who was filming us with Cheryl's phone, gave the cue to start. Everybody said what they were supposed to say and dumped the ice water on their heads. Then, Cheryl came over to me and poured a glass of ice cubes on my head. We were happy that we did the challenge!

"Where's the video?" my nurse who was filming us asked. "I can't find the video!" Cheryl looked for it on her

phone, but something went wrong. It didn't get recorded.
Cheryl's worst fear had come true. We had to do it all over
again! Cheryl, Phil, and Jane were good sports about it. And
me? What could I do? I got a second ice cube shower! Our
video is on YouTube. It is called *Man Who Has Lived With
ALS For 30 Years Takes #IceBucketChallenge.* If you want to see
it, you can go to YouTube or to our website at
www.oneblinkatatime.com and read our blog post called
Ismail and Cheryl Take the Ice Bucket Challenge.

I love the Ice Bucket Challenge. For the first time, most
people now know what ALS is, and donations keep pouring
in to the ALS Association. Within the first 30 days, the
association raised over $100 million in donations. $100
million! In one month! To defeat ALS! And the donations
continued coming in.

Some people complained that doing the challenge wasted
water. Other people said that the ALS Association did not
donate enough money to research. For these reasons they
refused to participate in the Ice Bucket Challenge. Even
worse, they said other people shouldn't do it either. Cheryl
and I responded to these criticisms in another blog post called
We Must Continue the Ice Bucket Challenge. Here's what we say
about wasting water:

> *It's true that there is a serious drought in the Western
> United States, especially in California, and we must all be
> diligent about saving water. That's why many participants
> are doing the challenge on their lawns, in other portions of
> their gardens, or standing in their swimming pools. No
> water wasted. We can raise awareness and help fund ALS
> research and be water-conscious at the same time.*

We also explained how donated funds are spent by the
ALS Association:

> *Financial Performance Metrics for the ALS Association
> and other charitable organizations can be found on Charity
> Navigator's website (www.charitynavigator-.org).
> According to their website, Charity Navigator is the nation's*

largest and most utilized evaluator of charities. They have awarded the ALS Association 4 stars for overall performance.

In addition to funding research, the ALS Association provides assistance for people with ALS through a nationwide network of chapters, coordinates multi-disciplinary care through Certified Treatment Centers of Excellence, and fosters government partnerships.

What many people might not know is that they can tell the ALS Association that they want their donation to go to research by going to **http://www.alsa.org/** and clicking on a box on the "DONATE" page that states "I want my donation to be used solely for ALS research." Even if they have already made a donation, they can still send an email requesting that the donation they made be spent for ALS research.

I thank everyone who dumped ice water over their heads and made donations to fight ALS. I hope that people will continue donating. Every dollar brings hope to people with ALS. Hope that maybe, after all these years, a cure for ALS will be found!

Surviving the Hospital

A sign points the way to a nearby hospital

Ismail's nurses and I do whatever we can to keep Ismail out of the hospital, including getting him a flu shot every year, keeping him away from sick people as much as possible, carefully monitoring him and increasing his breathing treatments and other special care as needed at the first sign of respiratory discomfort or potential cold or flu symptoms. We are dedicated to keeping Ismail out of the hospital for many reasons. First of all, hospitals breed bacteria and viruses that are dangerous to everyone, especially those who have weakened immune systems due to illnesses. Ismail is much more comfortable at home, where he can usually recover fairly quickly from manageable illnesses. He can remain in control of his care and activities of daily living when he's at home,

134

sleep in his own bed, watch television shows and movies of his choice on his big screen TV, and remain in the midst of the bustle of daily living.

Furthermore, Ismail has private duty nurses at home who care for him exclusively, so he gets constant, loving attention from caregivers he knows and trusts. His private duty nurses know how to communicate with him and can therefore better understand and attend to his needs than hospital nurses who do not have the time to learn his communication system. Our insurance company will not pay for his private duty nurses to provide care to him in a hospital because hospitals already provide their own nursing services.

Another reason it is safer for Ismail at home is that he is totally paralyzed and has no way of pushing a buzzer or hollering for help in an emergency. He once became disconnected from a ventilator while in a hospital and no one responded to the ventilator's alarm. Fortunately, I was in the room with him, and reconnected him to the ventilator.

Because I need to communicate with hospital staff for Ismail, make them aware of his needs, and advocate for him, whenever Ismail's in the hospital, I'm in there, too — 24 hours a day, seven days a week, until he's discharged. Being in the hospital 24/7 is exhausting and stressful. I hate being in the hospital as much as Ismail does.

Of course, there are times when we have no other option than to pack up Ismail's bags and drive him to the emergency room or, in times of extreme emergencies, call 911 and have the paramedics whisk him away. We have developed a hospital survival strategy for times when a hospital stay is necessary. We pack extra clothing, medical supplies, and all of Ismail's medications and vitamins and bring Ismail's own suction machine and ambu bag with us (even though the hospital will have its own equipment). Using his own home equipment makes Ismail feel more comfortable. We bring his home ventilator and vent supplies. Although the hospital usually insists on transferring Ismail to its own ventilator, he'll need to be transitioned back to his portable home ventilator when it's time for him to come home.

If I have time, I pack a bag for myself with extra clothing and personal items, such as a toothbrush, toothpaste, creams and lotions—everything I might pack if I were traveling out of town for 3-4 days. I also bring a folding lightweight cot. Negotiating use of the cot with nursing staff will make the difference between getting some sleep at night and suffering through several sleepless nights. I always resist the hospital's argument that there is a "comfortable" recliner in the room that I can sleep in. Believe me, these recliners are never truly comfortable and are almost always impossible to sleep in. A cot can be folded up and stored in a corner, out of the way of hospital staff, during the day.

A small laptop computer or DVD player can provide entertainment during long days in a hospital with limited television channels.

Whenever possible, I have one of Ismail's nurses accompany him in the ambulance, while I follow in our handicap van. That way, the van will be in the hospital's parking lot when it's time to bring Ismail home. The van also makes an excellent storage unit, when needed, for clothing and supplies.

For the most part, Ismail has received extraordinary hospital care. In the couple of instances where things did not go well, we learned valuable lessons and developed new hospital survival skills. Following are a few of our experiences. They illustrate the importance of having someone we trust stay with Ismail 24 hours a day every day he is in a hospital and speaking up when we have a need or questions about the care being provided to Ismail. They have proved the importance of refusing to listen to negative or dismissive talk by hospital staff and to fight for what we know is right. We never give up until we get what we need!

The Botched Trach Tube Change

When Ismail was new on the ventilator, I was responsible for changing his tracheotomy tube once a month. Not a big deal, I thought. Nothing could be easier. Take out the old tube, put in the new one. Still, ventilator care was new to me, so even though the procedure was simple, I felt a little anxious about doing it at home by myself. After all, we're talking about access to Ismail's airway, so the stakes were high.

In those early days, we didn't yet have regular, long-term nurses. Our nursing agency constantly sent out new nurses, some R.N.s, some L.V.N.s, depending on who was available. I'd always wait until the agency sent a nurse in whose experience and skills I had a lot of confidence and ask them to assist in the tube change. One night, the agency sent out an R.N. who had never been out to our home before, but who the agency said was an excellent nurse. I thought this would be a good opportunity to have the R.N. assist me in changing Ismail's trach tube. She seemed a little hesitant, but agreed. We decided that I'd change the tube, and she would assist me.

I got everything set up. Out with the old, in with the new. Quick. Easy. I took out the old tube. The new one wouldn't go in. This wasn't supposed to happen! I tried again. And again! I had the nurse try. She couldn't get it in, either. I called 911. We had a large oxygen tank in the bedroom that Ismail never used, but was there just in case. I unwound the extra-long tube that was connected to the tank and held the end of it to Ismail's tracheostomy, as if that would deliver oxygen to him. The nurse ran and got an ambu bag. Pushing aside the oxygen tube, she held the ambu bag to Ismail's tracheostomy and began pumping, trying to force air into him without the aid of a tube to transport the air to his lungs. Ismail sat there, looking calm, as the nurse and I ran around in full panic mode.

The paramedics arrived with red flashing lights and screaming sirens. They, too, tried to insert the trach tube. No luck. They lifted Ismail into the ambulance, the nurse still pumping uselessly on the ambu bag. Fortunately, the local emergency room was just a few of blocks from our house.

The staff at the emergency room tried to insert the tube. They couldn't get it in either. What was happening? Later, I learned that because Ismail's tracheostomy was so new, it had closed up quickly, and the trauma resulting from us repeatedly trying to jam in the plastic tube probably caused the surrounding tissues to swell, closing it up even more.

An anesthesiologist was called. He had trouble inserting the tube, too! After a couple of failed attempts, he forcefully jammed the tube into Ismail's throat. Blood splattered all over the room. Ismail hollered in agony. I screamed. A respiratory therapist connected Ismail to the ventilator and assured me he would be all right.

At a follow-up appointment, Dr. Oppenheimer told me the only reason Ismail survived that night was because he was still able to breathe on his own. Our efforts to deliver oxygen and air from an ambu bag without a trach tube in place were useless. Dr. Oppenheimer further explained that the most likely reason the tube wouldn't go in initially was because Ismail's head, which should have been tilted back, probably had not been positioned properly.

That was it. I was through changing trach tubes. From now on, I'd insist a physician change them in the safety of the clinic. Every month, I drove 35 miles each way to have Ismail's otolaryngologist, an ear, nose and throat specialist, perform the five-minute procedure. No amount of coaxing or encouragement would change my mind. I wouldn't do it. Never again!

It took several months and many practice runs with the doctor coaching me, to convince me to try the procedure again at home. I was terrified at first, but I took my time and was careful with every detail. I also had a nurse I trusted assist me. Thank God I never had another problem changing the tube. And the nurse who assisted me that terrifying night? Well, the trauma was apparently too much for her. She never came back.

Dropped On His Head

About eight years ago, I was doing some work in our family room when I heard Ismail's nurse holler from the bedroom "Oh! OHH!!" I rushed into the bedroom to find Ismail hanging upside down on his Hoyer lift, his head on the floor in a pool of blood! They've killed him! Then, I saw Ismail blink. Still alive! "Call 911!" I ordered the two male nurses standing frozen beside me. One was Ismail's regular caregiver, the other a nurse-in-training. "Call 911!" I repeated. "Never mind, I will." As I started to run out to call the paramedics, I saw Ismail's nurse begin to try to get him up. "Don't touch him!" I warned, afraid of a head or neck injury.

The 911 operator tried to keep me calm as she took information and dispatched an ambulance. I gasped out the facts. "Fell from a lift. Head bleeding. Lots of blood. Yes, he's breathing."

It always seems to take forever for an ambulance to arrive, even though in reality it only takes a few minutes. Of course, a few minutes can be an eternity when you're afraid your loved one is bleeding to death! When they got there, the paramedics examined Ismail and dressed his wound. They assured me head wounds always bleed profusely, that the huge amount of blood did not necessarily indicate a serious injury. They carried him out on a stretcher, his head wrapped in a bandage, his portable ventilator at his feet.

In the emergency room, they stitched up his wound and took a CT scan of his head. We waited...and waited for the results of the scan that would determine whether Ismail could go back home or would need to be admitted. In the meantime, they "observed" him. He lay propped up in the hospital bed, smiling at the nurses and spelling out answers to questions, as well as some questions of his own (When can we go home? When will they have the results of the test? When can we go home?)

The results of the scan showed a small amount of blood at the back of Ismail's brain. The emergency room nurse seemed perplexed. "Usually, when patients have blood in that area of their brain they are unconscious or in a state of extreme confusion," the nurse told me, "but look at him!" Ismail smiled back. Still, the troublesome blood warranted an overnight stay in the hospital, for observation. It was important to ensure that there was no active bleeding that would cause a dangerous amount of blood to pool in his brain. I asked about the danger of a blood clot forming. I was assured that risk was minimal. Fortunately, Ismail was stable enough to be transferred to our regular hospital 17 miles away.

While we waited for phone calls, paperwork, and the arrival of transportation, I left Ismail in the hands of the emergency room and his own private duty nurse to run home and pick up things we needed for an overnight hospital stay. When I returned to the emergency room, his private duty nurse asked me for Ismail's clothes so he could get him dressed. Ismail's clothes! That's right, he was naked when the paramedics took him off of the Hoyer lift and wrapped him up in a blanket for transporting. The one thing I had forgotten to pick up from home was his clothes! Couldn't we just keep him wrapped in a blanket? One look at my husband's face gave me the answer. He looked amazed and hurt that I could forget something as essential, as vital to his dignity as his clothes. Back to the house I went.

Ismail's private duty nurse was traumatized by the incident. He apologized over and over. One of the hooks on Ismail's sling had slipped off the lift's chain, he explained, and the sling gave way. I tried to assure him that the accident could have happened to anyone, but the nurse still felt personally responsible. He came with us to our regular hospital and insisted on continuing to care for Ismail late into the night, even though he knew he wouldn't be paid once Ismail was formally admitted to the hospital.

The night went smoothly. A CT scan taken the following morning showed no additional bleeding. Ismail was released with discharge instructions and a prescription for pain medication. To this day, he wears a scar on his forehead, a souvenir of the event. It's a small scar, right at his hairline, barely noticeable, but it's a reminder to all of us to take extra care during transfers.

Heart Attack?

I was getting Ismail ready to go to sleep one night a couple of years ago. Adjusting his pillows. Setting the level of warmth on his electric blanket. Repositioning his arms. For the past several months, he had been asking me to wrap his arms across his chest before he went to sleep. It seemed strange to me. I would think the pressure of his arms would press on his diaphragm and make breathing more difficult, but he always seemed perfectly comfortable, so I continued to wrap his arms around him every night. Tonight he told me he wanted his arms at his sides. I guess he's going back to his past sleeping position, I thought. I put his arms at his sides and finished his bedtime routine. He was having some shortness of breath. I adjusted the ventilator settings so that the machine would deliver increased amounts of air—just for a few minutes until he started to feel better. Then, he started to spell out "N-I-T-R-O-G-L...." Nitroglycerine? I was alarmed. "You want to take nitroglycerine?" He blinked once. Yes.

Nitroglycerine! It had been prescribed as a precaution when elevated levels on cardiac enzyme studies once indicated that he may have had a mild heart attack. May have. The diagnosis, which was made during a work-up for a different emergency, was not definitive because the elevated levels were "borderline" and could have been consistent with conditions other than a heart attack.

Just prior to his taking that test, we had a scary incident getting Ismail out of the van in the parking lot. As I was driving Ismail's wheelchair onto the automated lift at the side of the van, Ismail's jacket got caught on a small switch at the side of the lift and pushed it. The lift started to lower before his chair was all the way on it. I was unable to stop the lift, and it continued to go down. In an instant, Ismail's chair was tilted, halfway in the van and halfway on the lift as it continued to lower to the ground. The chair eventually crashed all the way onto the lift, and I was then able to drive the wheelchair off of it. Ismail was shaken up, but okay. I was shaken up, too! If the hospital had given me the cardiac enzyme studies that night, I probably would have tested positive for a heart attack, too! Anyway, as a result of those tests, he was prescribed nitroglycerine, just in case he ever needed it. He had been carrying a tiny bottle of the pills in his backpack for years, but he had never taken one before.

"If you need nitroglycerine, I have to call 911," I told him.

He blinked twice. No.

"I have to."

Two blinks.

I placed a nitroglycerine pill under his tongue and read the directions on the bottle: "Dissolve 1 tablet under the tongue as needed for chest pain. May repeat 2 times at 5-minute intervals. Call 911 if the pain persists longer than 5 minutes after the first dose. Continue to take the second and third dose if pain persists."

I waited five minutes, then put another pill under his tongue. " Do you still have pain?" I asked. Ismail blinked no. "Are you sure?" I persisted. One blink. "Are you saying that so I won't call 911?" I asked. A smile and another two blinks. "Please, please tell me if you start to have pain again. It's really important." Ismail agreed. "Is that why you didn't want your arms across your chest," I asked him, "because they were hurting your chest?" One blink. Yes.

I stayed up all night, watching him, taking his blood pressure every few minutes. His pressure started high, but gradually came down and stabilized. He didn't have a temperature. The truth is, I didn't want to call 911. I preferred to take him to our regular hospital instead of having him transported by ambulance to another facility. We had an unfortunate experience the last time that happened. A few years prior, he had been admitted with a staph infection to the ICU at a local community hospital. He had to stay overnight because the doctor said he wasn't stable enough to be transferred to our regular hospital. Several days and many diagnostic tests later, we were still there, and Ismail seemed to be getting sicker every day, becoming more and more bloated because of over-hydration. He looked like the Pillsbury Doughboy and developed fluid around his heart.

I was convinced Ismail would die if I didn't get him out of there. Whenever I asked that he be transferred, the doctor insisted he was not stable enough. I was afraid that he would never be stable again. His condition was deteriorating rapidly. One of the nurses cruelly told me he probably wouldn't make it because he was in kidney failure. When I protested that the results of a kidney test had just come back normal, she said "Oh, that doesn't mean anything. I've seen patients turn on a dime." Refusing to speak to that nurse again, I stepped up pressure to get him out of that hospital, complaining to everyone I could, making my own phone calls to our insurance company. Finally, a transfer was arranged. After a couple of days at our regular hospital, Ismail was back home, recovering, taking Lasix to get rid of the edema that continued to swell up his body.

The night Ismail complained about chest pain seemed to last an eternity. I sat beside him, monitoring him, watching for signs of chest pain, and counting the minutes until morning.

At six o'clock that morning, I called the nurse who was scheduled to be at our house at 7 a.m. "Ismail is very sick," I told her. "Is it possible for you to get here earlier than seven so we can rush him to the emergency room?"

The nurse arrived a few minutes later. She did an assessment and determined that Ismail indeed needed immediate medical attention. Ismail, being Ismail, insisted he needed a bath. Convincing him there was no time to spend on a bed bath, the nurse got him quickly dressed and ready to go.

I drove the van as quickly but safely as possible to the emergency room of our regular hospital, waiting impatiently at every red light. The emergency room staff examined him and ran lots of tests. "The good news is it's not his heart," the ER doctor told us. We were happy and relieved. "It's his gallbladder."

The doctor said Ismail was not a good candidate for surgery, but suggested a procedure they could try that would involve inserting a needle into the gallbladder and draining out the fluid. He said the procedure might relieve some of the symptoms. He then told us the surgeon wanted to talk to us.

Ismail and I both liked the surgeon the minute he walked in. He was a friendly doctor with a great bedside manner. He carefully explained to Ismail the benefits and risks of surgically removing his gallbladder. He was confident that he could remove the gallbladder with a laparoscopic procedure, which had fewer risks and a shorter recovery time than traditional surgery. He further explained that despite Ismail's ALS, he did not feel his risks were any greater than those of anyone else of his age group. Ismail's advantage was that he was already on a ventilator, eliminating one of the risk factors that others face.

Ismail had confidence in this physician. He blinked out a message for me to give him. "If you perform the surgery, I'll do it." I asked the surgeon if he would agree to do the surgery himself. He agreed, and the surgery was scheduled for the following day.

Sitting alone for two hours in the waiting room, I was a nervous wreck. Would Ismail tolerate the procedure? Would there be complications? Why is it taking so long? I watched other doctors come out and speak with the family members of other patients. I saw the families relieved at receiving good news and leave the waiting room. The room was becoming empty. It was lunchtime. Where was Ismail's surgeon? Did he forget me? Did something go wrong? When the surgeon came out, he brought good news. Everything went well. Ismail tolerated the surgery just fine. "It's a good thing we removed the gallbladder," he told me. "It was shriveled up and gangrenous."

Thank God Ismail decided to have the surgery and that this surgeon was willing to do it! Ismail survived!

My Most Terrifying Experience

The most terrifying experience for me in a hospital was in 2008. It started when Ismail was having severe abdominal pain, which we later learned was caused by diverticulitis. The doctors needed to do a CT Scan to determine what was causing the pain. The test required that they give Ismail contrast dye through his feeding tube. Ismail refused the dye because he was having extreme pain every time anyone gave him anything through his feeding tube. The doctor insisted that the test was necessary, so the nurse proceeded to give him the contrast dye, a little every few minutes. Ismail immediately began having severe abdominal pain. His blood pressure shot up. He became short of breath.

During the set-up for the scan, the respiratory therapist complained that the ventilator in the x-ray room was not working properly, that the numbers wouldn't stabilize. He brought in the ventilator from Ismail's room and hooked him up to that one, but the same problem occurred with that machine as well. The therapist blamed the problem on air leakage around Ismail's trach tube. They completed the CT scan anyway and returned Ismail to his room.

Ismail continued to suffer from intense pain and shortness of breath and the readings of his hospital ventilator continued to be unstable. I had discussions with the hospital staff about whether we should change Ismail's trach tube to a cuffed one, which would have a small inflated balloon that would seal up the airway and stop the air leak, or to transfer Ismail to his portable home ventilator which routinely compensated for his air leakage. Unfortunately, his home ventilator sat in our house nearly 20 miles away. Ismail protested to having his trach tube changed. I offered to drive home to pick up his home ventilator if the hospital could arrange for someone to stay at Ismail's bedside while I was gone. By the time arrangements were made for someone to sit with Ismail, his shortness of breath had become so bad and his condition so unstable that I no longer felt comfortable leaving him. I convinced Ismail to let them change his trach tube.

The trach tube change was difficult and painful for Ismail, but it was finally accomplished. However Ismail's respiratory distress continued.

He was now constantly requiring more frequent breaths administered with the ambu bag. I feared he was developing acidosis, a dangerous, potentially fatal condition resulting from increased acidity in the blood. I remembered that when Ismail had acidosis before and was admitted to a local hospital, a medical professional there told me that acidosis creates a sense of air hunger and giving more breaths with an ambu bag to ease the air hunger worsens the acidosis. A vicious cycle. I knew the symptoms well. Ismail nearly died of acidosis that time. I refused to give him more puffs with the ambu bag, but his eyes were desperate as he begged. I pleaded with him. He begged until I relented. The situation became so bad that I was unable to stop the bagging—as soon as I would stop giving him puffs, he would beg for more.

I called for the respiratory therapist and asked him to do an arterial blood gas (a special blood test that could measure the pH of Ismail's blood and determine whether he was indeed in a state of acidosis). The respiratory therapist argued that an arterial blood gas was done at 1:00 p.m. and that it was "perfect." "It is now 9:00 p.m.," I said, "and a lot has happened in the meantime."

Eventually, I convinced the therapist that I knew the symptoms of acidosis from previous experience, and he agreed to see whether the doctor would approve another arterial blood gas. He returned in a few minutes and drew the blood. A little while later, he came back. "I have to admit that was a good call on your part," he said. Ismail desperately pleaded for the ambu bag. I tried to verbally comfort him. He continued to be in terrible respiratory distress. His agony and my fear of acidosis tore me apart. "The last time this happened, Ismail was started immediately on sodium bicarbonate to balance the pH in his blood," I told the therapist.

"The doctor is aware of that treatment," he responded. "He wants to wait an hour and repeat the blood test before deciding on a plan of treatment."

Wait an hour! I looked at Ismail who was in total agony, still begging for the ambu bag. "Why?" I demanded. The therapist gave me one of those "doctor knows best" looks and repeated that they were going to wait and do another blood gas in an hour.

A nurse gave Ismail a small dose of morphine. Ismail began to quiet down and grow drowsy. He eventually fell asleep. Thank goodness, I thought, he's comfortable now. After the repeat arterial blood gas, I asked the respiratory therapist what the result was. "The same," he said. "The acidosis has not improved." I asked whether they were going to start the sodium bicarbonate. He said they were going to wait. Wait? Ismail was asleep now and looking comfortable. Maybe the crisis had passed, I hoped.

Eventually, I fell asleep in the recliner next to Ismail. During the night, I heard a nurse come into the room and talk to him. In the morning, I saw someone come in and draw blood. At 6:00 a.m., I noticed that Ismail seemed to still be sleeping very soundly. I hesitated waking him up. He really needed rest, but he was usually awake by this time. I leaned over the bed and spoke to him. He didn't respond. I shook him slightly. "Ismail?" I raised my voice. "Ismail? Ismail?" No response. I ran out into the hall. "Nurse! Nurse! My husband's not responding!"

The nurse looked at me quizzically. "What do you mean?"

"He's not responding!"

A couple of nurses rushed into the room. They couldn't arouse him either.

A doctor came in and examined Ismail. "His pupils are not responding to light," she told me. "He is not responding to pain." She asked the nurse when the last time was that Ismail had responded to her. The nurse said 4:00 a.m. "He might have had a stroke sometime between 4:00 a.m. and 6:00 a.m.," the doctor told me.

"What would have triggered a stroke?" I asked, angry and terrified, not believing her.

"People have strokes all the time," she said.

They rushed Ismail back to Radiology to do another CT scan—this time of his brain. They made me wait outside the room. I sat in the waiting room with a close friend, a member of our extended family. I had called her because I felt totally alone and afraid and needed to talk to someone. I knew she would be there for us. "I did this," I confessed to her. "I shouldn't have given him the ambu bag. I should have been stronger. And I knew better! I knew better, but I did it anyway! Why did I do it? I killed him!" I was sobbing.

"Stop that!" she said. "Don't say that! Don't even think it! You have to stay positive."

She walked with me as I paced in front of the radiology lab door. Why wouldn't they let me inside? It seemed to take forever to find out whether my husband was dead or alive. When the door finally opened at the conclusion of the test, I saw the technician shake his head at a nurse. His lips formed the word "Nothing." No brain activity, I thought. He's gone. My heart ached as the walls of the hospital closed in on me. I gave him the ambu bag. Now he's dead. Later the nurse told me that shake of the technician's head meant there were no abnormalities found on the test. Not dead! There was still hope!

Back in his hospital room, I talked to Ismail, read to him, continued to try to get him to respond. Another doctor came in and examined him. She turned off the overhead lights and shined a flashlight in his eyes. "His pupils are responding to light," she said. I gasped. I felt like dancing around the room. He's responding! He's responding! I sang the words in my head. "But the response is very weak. You have to turn off the overhead lights to see it." She continued her examination, but Ismail had no other responses. I was glad when she told me they were going to transfer him to ICU. He would get close attention and great care there.

In ICU, a stream of specialists stopped by to examine him. One doctor explained that Ismail had developed diabetic ketoacidosis, hypotension and shock. Another doctor gently explained that I was mistaken about how using the ambu bag affected Ismail's condition. "It is the acidosis that creates the air hunger and need for additional ventilation," he said. "Giving additional breaths with the ambu bag does not cause or worsen the acidosis." A huge burden of guilt lifted off of me.

I continued to talk to Ismail, ask him questions, looking for any sign of a response. Finally, there it was! A blink! An answer to my question: "Can you hear me?" But did I really see it? It was so very, very weak. "Can you hear me?" I asked him again. Yes! There it was again! A minute flicker of his eyelid, but a definite blink. At that moment, a neurologist arrived to examine him. "He's responding!" I blurted out. "He blinked in response to a question!" The neurologist looked at me with sympathetic skepticism.

"Was it an appropriate response?" he asked.

"Yes!" My excitement bubbled over.

I explained our eye blink communication system to him, how Ismail could respond "yes" to his questions by blinking once and "no" to his questions by blinking twice. "His blink is very weak," I warned. "You have to look very closely."

He asked me to wait outside the room while he conducted his examination. I could hear him asking Ismail questions. "Yes, he is responding," the neurologist confirmed when he emerged from the room. "Since he's beginning to come out of his coma this quickly, he has a good chance of making a full recovery."

I dissolved into tears of joy. Ismail was coming back to me!

My Latest Challenge

Ismail celebrating the completion of the first draft of *One Blink at a Time*

As my life progresses, I continue to be faced by new challenges. That's expected. After all, challenges are an important part of life. We face them, we resolve them, we learn from them.

The years 2013 and 2014 brought Cheryl and me one of the biggest and most satisfying challenges of our lives: writing this book.

One of the most challenging things for me was trying to remember in detail each situation I wrote about, describing where it happened and how it happened. Fortunately, I have always had an excellent memory. I can remember specific details about incidents and dates from long ago. Cheryl always says she relies on me to be her brain when it comes to details and dates.

I would work out the details of an incident in my head, then spell it out to Cheryl. Sometimes, it took me all day to spell out a single page. We had to stop frequently to allow my nurses time to feed me, suction me, transfer me to the bed I lie down in each afternoon, and do other things related to my daily care.

When I get tired, it becomes harder for me to blink my eye. Sometimes, Cheryl and I had to stop for a while because she could no longer see my weak eye blinks. Although it's sometimes tiring for me to blink my eye, I know that Cheryl and I will find new ways for me to continue to communicate and work on books and other projects. I'll never give up my fight.

Writing this book has been a real challenge, but it has been worth it. I hope it will be helpful and informative for other people in situations such as mine and will educate the general public about this deadly disease, ALS.

Outliving Our Equipment

Cheryl and Ismail at the Ventura County Walk to Defeat ALS in 2013

In the early years of our journey, we worked with physical therapists, wheelchair providers, and companies that provide Durable Medical Equipment (DME) to identify the most appropriate and efficient equipment to meet Ismail's needs. As a result, Ismail has high-quality equipment that has served him well for more than 20 years. Unfortunately, equipment doesn't last forever. Replacing it can be painful.

Ismail likes the equipment he has. He's comfortable with it. He has confidence in it. He wants to hold onto it as long as he can.

The Wheelchair That Keeps on Rolling

Ismail's motorized wheelchair has a fully-adjustable head support system, adjustable arm and foot rests, and a ventilator tray in back that swings out to hold his ventilator securely each time the back of his wheelchair is reclined. The chair was custom-made for Ismail, and he has been comfortable in it for many years.   "This wheelchair is getting very old," the technician who comes to our home to repair the wheelchair often says.   "I don't know how much longer I'll be able to continue to get parts for it. Ismail is not going to like the new wheelchairs we have available.   I know Ismail. He likes his chair. I hope it lasts a long time."

We continue to extend the chair's life by repairing parts that can no longer be replaced. How much longer will we be able to do that? Who knows. We'll continue to keep Ismail's chair running as long as we can.

The Spare-Parts Hoyer Lift

We're doing the same with his Hoyer lift, a simple, but efficient machine. We connect Ismail to it by attaching the hooks on a sling we place under him to the chains on a cradle that hangs from the lift's arm. We manually crank up the arm to raise Ismail out of his bed or wheelchair, and then lower the lift's arm to place him into his bed or onto his commode. The base of the lift has wheels so we can easily push the lift around the house. It is u-shaped so that it can wrap around the front of a wheelchair or commode. The lift works well in small spaces, such as the area in our bedroom that we use for transferring Ismail from his wheelchair into his bed.

Since the lift is no longer being manufactured, we're no longer able to get new parts for it. When its wheels recently wore out, our DME provider delivered a new model lift to our home. It had a hydraulic system that potentially made it easy for our caregivers to raise and lower the arm of the lift at the push of a button. When we attempted to use it, we realized it would never work out. The base of the lift spread open like giant jaws poised to devour the wheelchair in front of it. It was too big—much too big— and required too much operating space to fit in our bedroom. We tried other models. Nothing worked. Fortunately, we have an identical lift to the one we currently use stored in our garage. The DME company let us keep the extra lift because it is old and broken and can no longer be used. Like harvesting organs for a transplant, we took wheels off the extra lift and put them on the one we have in service. Voila! Fixed!

The Van That's Younger Than It Looks

Our 1989 van has faded paint and wears dents like small scars. Rust dots its body like old age spots. Worn-out rubber lining sticks out of its windows and doors. The air conditioner died many years ago. So did the radio. But the van continues to run like new. It should. Despite its age, it has only 72,000 miles on it. We've had to buy new tires a number of times because the van sits outside, and rubber doesn't hold up well in California's sun and heat. Otherwise, minor repairs and regular maintenance has kept our handicap van going all these years. We love our van. We expect it to continue to get us where we need to go for a long time to come.

Updating Our Ventilator

The ventilator that Ismail used for many years was no longer being manufactured, and the DME company could no longer get parts to service it. So, the company made arrangements for Ismail to be transitioned to a newer type of ventilator. Ismail and I and one of our nurses spent an afternoon in the clinic having Ismail try out the new ventilator and tweaking the settings until he felt comfortable. The nurse and I were trained on the new machine that day, and an in-service training with a respiratory therapist was scheduled in our home for all of the other nurses on our case. We soon learned that the new ventilator was not going to work out for Ismail.

We tried out the ventilator for more than six months. There were many irresolvable problems. For example, the ventilator's menu system was time-consuming and not user-friendly for some of our caregivers. Also the alarm wasn't loud enough for a caregiver in another room to hear. The alarms for various problems (high pressure, low pressure, disconnect) all sounded similar to one another, so we couldn't identify the problem simply by the sound of the alarm. This could be a potential patient safety issue. Since Ismail uses an uncuffed trach tube, there is always air leakage around his trach, and the model of the new ventilator we were given (unlike our previous one) did not have leak compensation, so alarms were going off constantly (we were unable to sleep at night when he was using that ventilator). Most of the time, the alarms required no action.

Ismail was unable to create enough pressure to make the ventilator beep, so his method of calling us by making the ventilator to beep twice would not work. Since the machine was beeping all the time anyway, it would have been impossible for us to recognize when Ismail was doing it on purpose.

Still another issue was that the size and shape of the new ventilator was not compatible with the tray attached to the back of Ismail's power wheelchair. The machine had to be hung in a backpack on a handle at the rear of the wheelchair and removed every time we had to recline the back of the chair to reposition Ismail. We then had to hang it back on the handle once we brought the back of the wheelchair up again. What a hassle.

The DME company insisted that we keep trouble-shooting the problems, even though we had already exhausted all troubleshooting options. Finally, months later, with the assistance of Dr. Luis Moreta-Sainz, another great pulmonologist we were lucky to get after Dr. Oppenheimer retired, we were able to try a different model ventilator. Ismail and I had to stay overnight in the hospital so that Ismail could be observed and his comfort and safety could be monitored. It was worth it. Ismail came home on a different model ventilator. The new machine solved all of the problems we were having with the other one, and we love it!

Thanksgiving

Ismail and Cheryl in 1970

Cheryl and I have three celebrations at Thanksgiving time every year. First, we celebrate the Thanksgiving holiday with our family. Even though I cannot eat the food served at the big turkey feast along with everyone else, I love this holiday because I get to see many of our relatives, including some of my grandnieces and grandnephews who run around and make a lot of noise. They are so happy and full of fun! I also like Thanksgiving because it is a day to remember all the things we have to be thankful for.

I'm thankful for many things, especially my long life, in spite of having ALS, and the gift of every new day. I'm thankful for the enjoyment and surprises that life continues to bring. I'm thankful for my warm and comfortable home, for my loving family, who is always there for me, and for my friends who love me, support me, and care about me. I'm grateful for the compassion, support, friendship, and excellent care I receive every day from my wonderful nurses and for the outstanding medical care I receive from my awesome team of doctors and other medical care providers. I'm lucky to have kind neighbors who look out for Cheryl and me. I'm grateful to have the ability to continue to work with Cheryl on creative projects such as Honest Course, new plays and musicals, and this book. Most of all, I'm thankful for my 44 happy years of marriage with Cheryl and the ability to survive and be happy, year after year.

In addition to the traditional Thanksgiving Day holiday, Cheryl and I celebrate our Thanksgiving Day wedding anniversary (November 26, 1970) and the anniversary of my tracheotomy (November 26, 1990). On November 26, 2014, Cheryl and I had our own private party at home — just the two of us — to celebrate both the 44th anniversary of our wedding and the 24th anniversary of the day I began using a ventilator. We enjoyed quiet, quality time together, watching good movies and eating Greek food. Cheryl ordered my favorite dish, Moussaka, from our local Greek restaurant.

I love Greek food and introduced Cheryl to it when we first started dating. She learned how to cook great Greek food and used to make it several times a year. However, since Moussaka takes many hours to prepare and our local restaurant makes excellent authentic Greek food, Cheryl now usually saves time and orders from them. My nurse put a big portion of the casserole into a blender with a little water and a tiny bit of red wine and blended it until it was a smooth consistency that she could push through my G-tube. I know it's hard for a lot of people to believe, but I can actually taste food that is given to me through my G-tube. Our special anniversary dinner was delicious!

In 1998, I wrote an article called "A Happy Anniversary." It was published in the Winter, 1998 edition of "Ventilator Assisted Living," a publication of International Ventilator Users Network (IVUN). The article can be found at the following link: **http://www.ventusers.org/edu/valnews/val12-4b.html.** In the article, I talk about our two anniversaries and my life living at home with a ventilator. I explain that Cheryl and I have shared challenging but happy years "...enjoying many wonderful times, facing problems, and overcoming obstacles together. To say it has not always been easy would be an understatement. Often, life has been downright hard." We could not have made it without a lot of help from our friends, our family, our many nurses, my health care team, and my fantastic physicians. "Would we do it all over again?" I ask at the end of the article. "You bet we would." After all, the ventilator has enabled Cheryl and me to be together all these years. At the end of the article I write: "We look forward to spending many more years, many more anniversaries and Thanksgivings together."

Cheryl and I feel the same way today as we look forward to a happy future together.

How I've Made It

Ismail kisses his bride, November 26, 1970

"How do you do it?" people frequently ask me. "How have you survived being a caregiver for your husband for thirty years?" Some people say I'm a heroine. I'm not. Others say I'm a super-woman. No way.

How have I made it through these thirty years?

I have made it because Ismail, despite his illness, the pain he suffers every day, and his physical limitations, continues to enjoy life and be upbeat, good-natured, and loving. Ismail and I have as much respect and affection for one another as we did the day we were married. I want and need him with me. I would do anything in the world to help him and keep him close to me. I love being with him, writing with him, watching good movies with him, and going out with him to our favorite summertime places. We enjoy one another's company. If our marriage and mutual commitment hadn't been as strong as it was before Ismail developed symptoms of ALS, if Ismail had become angry at his disease and had taken it out on me, if he had grown morose, surly, or felt sorry for himself, we may not have made it this long. But we are one another's rock, and together we'll keep going.

I have made it because Ismail and I traveled this journey one step at a time and tackled our challenges one problem at a time. If someone had told me when Ismail was first diagnosed that I would be his caregiver for thirty years, I would have felt completely overwhelmed. I don't know whether I would have had the inner strength to face that daunting challenge. Since we didn't know how long our journey would be, we took it one day at a time, and the years passed. I grew stronger and more self-confident as time went by. And here we are, thirty years later, still going strong. Like other couples who have been married 44 years, we wonder "Where has the time gone?"

I have made it because of the help I get from the wonderful team of nurses who provide care and friendship to Ismail 16 hours a day, 7 days a week. I will forever be grateful to our insurance company for paying for this care. I don't know how I could have survived without it, and we could never afford to pay for it ourselves. Because we are blessed to have nursing care for Ismail, I have been able to work full-time and pursue professional and personal interests of my own, to get needed respite from time to time, and to have backup assistance in difficult and dangerous times.

Finally, I have made it because our awesome team of doctors and other medical care providers keeps Ismail and me healthy and strong, because our loving family is always there for us, because our friends love us and support us and care about us, and because our kind neighbors look out for us.

What Keeps Me Going

Family and friends celebrate Ismail's birthday, January 2014

People are amazed that I have survived ALS for thirty years and still feel good and enjoy life. They want to know how I've done it. They ask me how I can continue to wake up every morning, totally paralyzed and unable to talk or to eat, and still want to go on after so many years. The answer is simple. I have a lot to live for.

I love my wife and enjoy being with her. She is my best friend and collaborator. I want to continue to be with her as long as I can.

I have the greatest team of doctors in the world who keep me healthy and feeling good.

My fantastic nurses help me with the care I need for daily living. They keep me company, play music for me, and watch television with me. They accompany Cheryl and me to doctors' and dentists' appointments, to ALS walks, and on all kinds of fun outings. It would be very difficult for Cheryl and me to go out without the help of my nurses. I would not be as happy if I had to stay at home all the time. I plan to continue to go out and have fun as long as I am able.

I have the greatest family and friends in the world. They stick by me and love me for what I am. I have enjoyed watching my nieces and nephew grow up, and I'm happy to see my grandnieces and grandnephews playing together. I look forward to watching them grow up, too.

I don't spend time feeling sorry for myself. What could I get by crying or feeling sorry for myself? I'd only get pain and misery. I accept things for what they are. I focus on what I can do, not what I can't do. I can still enjoy good movies and my favorite television shows. I can still communicate with my caregivers and my friends. With eye blink, I can still write blogs and Facebook posts. I can write plays and musicals with Cheryl. I wrote chapters for this book. With patience and determination, we can overcome any obstacles that life presents, including communication challenges.

I enjoy special visits from friends, and I love celebrations. On our 40th wedding anniversary, Cheryl invited many of our friends, relatives, and neighbors over for an anniversary celebration. It was a great party. Since I don't frequently get out to neighborhood parties, this was the first time I had seen some of our neighbors in many years. We had another neighborhood get-together at our home in December, 2013. It was a lot of fun. I got to meet a young couple who had moved into our neighborhood a few months prior and saw another couple that I hadn't seen in many years.

The following January, I celebrated my birthday with friends and relatives. What made this birthday special was a very big surprise cooked up by Cheryl. She brought Phil and Jane out from New York. We hadn't seen them for several years. We celebrated and enjoyed their company for a whole week. Phil brought with him a 16mm film that he and I had worked on in 1971. I wrote and directed the promo, and Phil did the cinematography. Phil had the film transferred onto a DVD so we could watch it together after all these years. It was a great trip down Memory Lane! I am happy that I can still participate in special celebrations like these, and I want to live to enjoy many more of them.

Finally, I want to go on living because I still have dreams. I dream of living many more years with Cheryl, of writing more books, musicals, and other projects with her, and with the publication of this book, giving other people in situations like mine encouragement and hope.

Appendices

Appendix A
Chronology

Date	Milestone
1960s	Ismail's first symptoms of muscle pain and weakness began
Late 1960s	Doctor prescribes neck collar for Ismail's neck pain and weakness
Nov. 26, 1970	Ismail and Cheryl's wedding
1974	Ismail and Cheryl go on Carribean cruise and Mardi Gras in New Orleans
1976	Weakness beings in Ismail's right arm
1980	Ismail unable to hold infant niece in his arms
1987	Ismail diagnosed with ALS
1988	Ismail gets foot-controller for editing equipment
1989	Ismail and Cheryl take European tour
Nov. 26, 1990	Ismail has tracheotomy Ismail & Cheryl's 20th wedding anniversary
1991	*It's Your Choice* video produced
1992	Ismail and Cheryl get handicap van
Aug. 14, 1992	Ismail and Cheryl meet Stephen Hawking
1993	*Caring For the Caregiver* video and training materials produced *What is ALS?* video co-produced with ALS Association
Jan. 17, 1994	Northridge Earthquake
Nov. 23, 1995	Ismail and Cheryl renew their 25-year wedding vows

1995	Ismail's gastrostomy tube (G-tube or feeding tube) inserted
1998	Cheryl's first out-of-state trip away from home Ismail gets power wheelchair
Oct. 25, 2003	Simi Valley fire
2003	Begin using two nursing agencies at the same time
2005	Ismail and Cheryl participate in their first Walk to Defeat ALS
July 2012	Cheryl's retirement
May 2014	Cheryl goes to the ALS Association's Annual Public Policy Conference in Washington, DC and goes to Capital Hill
July 2014	Ismail signs up to be an early adopter of EyeSpeak
December 2014	Publication of *One Blink at a Time*

Appendix B
Glossary

Term	Definition
Acidosis	Respiratory acidosis develops when there is too much carbon dioxide (an acid) in the body. This type of acidosis is usually caused when the body is unable to remove enough carbon dioxide through breathing. Other names for respiratory acidosis are hypercapnic acidosis and carbon dioxide acidosis. **http://www.nlm.nih.gov/medlineplus/ency/article/001181.htm**
Adult Day Care Center	An adult day care center, also commonly known as adult day services, is a non-residential facility that supports the health, nutritional, social support, and daily living needs of adults in professionally staffed, group settings. **http://en.wikipedia.org.wiki/Adult_daycare_center**
ALS Research Program at Dept. of Defense (ALSRP)	Military veterans are diagnosed at approximately twice the rate of the general public. Because of this, the ALS Association worked with Congress and the Department of Defense (DOD) to create the ALSRP in 2007. ALSRP is the only ALS-specific program at DOD and is specifically focused on finding new treatments for the disease. The association has helped to secure more than $40 million in Congressional funding for the program. **http://www.alsa.org/news/archive/alsrp-awards-2014.html**
Alternating air pressure mattress	Air mattress that is placed on top of a regular bed mattress; used to promote skin integrity and prevent skin breakdown; has air-filled channels that alternately fill and empty to keep

bearing weight off bony prominences of immobilized or weak patients who are unable to shift their weight frequently.
http://medical-dictionary.thefreedictionary. com/alternating+pressure+air+mattress

Ambu bag

A bag valve mask, abbreviated to BVM and sometimes known by the proprietary name Ambu bag or generically as a manual resuscitator or 'self-inflating bag', is a hand-held device commonly used to provide positive pressure ventilation to patients who are not breathing or not breathing adequately.
http://en.wikipedia.org/wiki/Bag_valve_mask

Amyotrophic Lateral Sclerosis (ALS)

Amyotrophic lateral sclerosis (ALS) is a progressive neurodegenerative disease that affects nerve cells in the brain and the spinal cord. Motor neurons reach from the brain to the spinal cord and from the spinal cord to the muscles throughout the body. The progressive degeneration of the motor neurons in ALS eventually leads to their death. When the motor neurons die, the ability of the brain to initiate and control muscle movement is lost. With voluntary muscle action progressively affected, patients in the later stages of the disease may become totally paralyzed.
http://www.alsa.org/about-als/

Anesthesiologist

A physician trained in anesthesia and peri-operative medicine. In the United States, the term anesthesiologist refers to a physician who completed an accredited residency program in anesthesiology, usually four years following medical school either with M.D. or D.O. degree. In contrast, the term anesthetist is used for nurse anesthesia providers who have undergone specialized training in anesthesia.
http://en.wikipedia.org/wiki/Anesthesiologist

Arterial blood gas

An arterial blood gas (ABG) test measures the acidity (pH) and the levels of oxygen and carbon dioxide in the blood from an artery. This test is used to check how well your lungs are able to move oxygen into the blood and remove carbon dioxide from the blood. **http://www.webmd.com/lung/arterial-blood-gases**

Artificial prosthesis In medicine, a prosthesis...is an artificial device that replaces a missing body part, which may be lost through trauma, disease, or congenital conditions. Prosthetic amputee rehabilitation is coordinated by an inter-disciplinary team of health care professionals including physiatrists and prosthetists. **http://en.wikipedia.org/wiki/Prosthesis**

Augmentative Communication Augmentative and alternative commication, also known as AAC, is a term that is used to describe various methods of communication that can help people who are unable to use verbal speech to communicate. AAC can benefit a wide range of individuals, from a beginning communicator to a more sophisticated communicator who generates his own messages. AAC includes both unaided and aided systems. Unaided systems, like signing and gestures, do not require special materials or equipment. Aided systems use picture charts, books and special computers. AAC methods vary and may be personalized to meet each individual's needs. Many forms of AAC include an assistive technology component which range from high- to low-tech strategies. **http://www.prentrom.com/what-is-augmentative-and-alternative-communication**

Bowel obstruction A bowel obstruction happens when either your small or large intestine is partly or completely blocked. The blockage prevents food, fluids, and gas from moving through the intestines in the normal way. The blockage may cause severe pain that comes and

goes....Tumors, scar tissue (adhesions), or twisting or narrowing of the intestines can cause a bowel obstruction. These are called mechanical obstructions.
http://www.webmd.com/digestive-disorders/tc/bowel-obstruction-topic-overview

Brain-computer interface (BCI) technology	Brain-computer interface (BCI) is a collaboration between a brain and a device that enables signals from the brain to direct some external activity, such as control of a cursor or a prosthetic limb. The interface enables a direct communications pathway between the brain and the object to be controlled. In the case of cursor control, for example, the signal is transmitted directly from the brain to the mechanism directing the cursor, rather than taking the normal route through the body's neuromuscular system from the brain to the finger on a mouse. **http://whatis.techtarget.com/definition/brain-computer-interface-BCI**
CALS	Caregiver for a person with ALS.
Centers for Medicare and Medicaid Services (CMS)	The Centers for Medicare & Medicaid Services (CMS), previously known as the Health Care Financing Administration (HCFA), is a federal agency within the United States Department of Health and Human Services (DHHS) that administers the Medicare program and works in partnership with state governments to administer Medicaid, the State Children's Health Insurance Program (SCHIP), and health insurance portability standards. In addition to these programs, CMS has other responsibilities, including the administrative simplification standards from the Health Insurance Portability and Accountability Act of 1996 (HIPAA), quality standards in long-term care facilities (more commonly referred to as nursing homes) through its survey and

certification process, clinical laboratory quality standards under the Clinical Laboratory Improvement Amendments, and oversight of HealthCare.gov.
http://en.wikipedia.org/wiki/Centers_for_ Medicaid_and_Medicaid_Services

Charity Navigator

Charity Navigator is an organization that evaluates charities. Its website states that Charity Navigator has become the nation's largest and most utilized evaluation of charities. It estimates that it has examined tens of thousands of non-profit financial documents and says it has used this knowledge to develop an unbiased, objective, numbers-based rating system to assess over 7,000 of America's best-known and some lesser known, but worthy, charities.
http://www.charitynavigator.org/

Circuitry

Ventilator circuits are tubes of various types which are utilized by medical ventilators in the application of mechanical ventilation.
http://en.wikipedia.org/wiki/Ventilator_ circuit

Colonoscopy

A colonoscopy is a test that allows a doctor to look at the inner lining of a patient's large intestine (rectum and colon). The physician uses a thin, flexible tube called a colonoscope to look at the colon. A colonoscopy helps find ulcers, colon polyps, tumors, and areas of inflammation or bleeding. During a colonoscopy, tissue samples can be collected (biopsy) and abnormal growths can be taken out. Colonoscopy can also be used as a screening test to check for cancer or precancerous growths in the colon or rectum (polyps).
http://www.webmd.com/colorectal-cancer/ colonoscopy-16695

Commode chair

A commode chair is a portable toilet that can be placed at the bedside of a patient whose activity is limited; these are often used in the home when the patient is too debilitated to reach the bathroom. The receptacle for waste can be removed and emptied. **http://medical-dictionary.thefreedictionary.com/commode+chair**

Contrast dye

Radiocontrast agents are a type of medical contrast medium used to improve the visibility of internal bodily structures in X-ray based imaging techniques such as computed tomography (CT) and radiography (commonly known as X-ray imaging). Radiocontrast agents are typically iodine or barium compounds. **http://encyclopedia.thefreedictionary.com/Contrast+dye**

CT scan

Computerized tomography (CT scan)—also called CT—combines a series of X-ray views taken from many different angles and computer processing to create cross-sectional images of the bones and soft tissues inside your body. **http://www.mayoclinic.org/tests-procedures/ct-scan/basics/definition/prc-20014610**

Diabetic Ketoacidosis

Diabetic ketoacidosis is a life-threatening problem that affects people with diabetes. It occurs when the body cannot use sugar (glucose) as a fuel source because there is no insulin or not enough insulin. Fat is used for fuel instead. When fat breaks down, waste products called ketones build up in the body. Causes: As fat is broken down, acids called ketones build up in the blood and urine. In high levels, ketones are poisonous. This condition is known as ketoacidosis. Diabetic ketoacidosis is often the first sign of type 1 diabetes in people who do not yet have other symptoms. It can also occur in someone who has already been diagnosed with type 1 diabetes. Infection, injury, a serious illness, missing doses of insulin shots, or surgery can lead to diabetic ketoacidosis in people with type 1 diabetes. People with type 2 diabetes can also develop ketoacidosis, but it is less common. It is usually triggered by uncontrolled blood sugar or a severe illness. **http://www.nlm.nih.gov/medlineplus/ency/a rticle/000320.htm**

Diaphragm	Dome-shaped muscular and membranous structure between the thoracic and abdominal cavities. The principal muscle used in respiration, it is also important in coughing, vomiting, excretion, and other expulsive functions. Spasms of the diaphragm produce hiccups. The aorta passes behind the diaphragm; the inferior vena cava and esophagus pass through it. Protrusion of part of the stomach above the diaphragm is called a hiatal hernia. **http://www.merriam-webster.com/ dictionary/diaphragm**
Durable medical equipment (DME)	Durable medical equipment is any medical equipment used in the home to aid in a better quality of living. It is a benefit included in most insurances. In some cases certain Medicare benefits, that is, whether Medicare may pay for the item. The item is defined by Title XIX for Medicaid. **http://en.wikipedia.org/wiki/Durable_ medical_equipment**
Early adopter	A person who uses a new product or technology before it becomes widely known or used. **http://dictionary.reference.com/browse/ early+adopter**
Electromyography (EMG)	Electromyography (EMG) is a diagnostic procedure to assess the health of muscles and the nerve cells that control them (motor neurons). Neurons transmit electrical signals that cause muscles to contract. An EMG

translates these signals into graphs, sounds or numerical values that a specialist interprets. An EMG uses tiny devices called electrodes to transmit or detect electrical signals. During a needle EMG, a needle electrode inserted directly into a muscle records the electrical activity in that muscle. A nerve conduction study, another part of an EMG, uses electrodes taped to the skin (surface electrodes) to measure the speed and strength of signals traveling between two or more points. EMG results can reveal nerve dysfunction, muscle dysfunction or problems with nerve-to-muscle signal transmission.
http://www.mayoclinic.org/tests-proce dures/electroconvulsive-therapy/basics /definition/prc-20014183

Endoscopic mucosal resection

Gastrointestinal endoscopic mucosal resection (EMR) is a procedure to remove cancerous or other abnormal tissues (lesions) from the digestive tract. Endoscopic mucosal resection is performed with a long, narrow tube equipped with a light, video camera and other instruments. During EMR of the upper digestive tract, the tube (endoscope) is passed down your throat to reach an abnormality in your esophagus, stomach or upper part of the small intestine (duodenum). To remove lesions from the colon, the tube is guided up through the anus.
http://www.mayoclinic.org/testsproce dures/endoscopicmucosalresection- /basics/definition/prc-20014197

Environmental Control

An environmental control system is a form of electronic assistive technology which enables people with significant disabilities to independently access equipment in their environment, e.g. home or hospital.
http://en.wikipedia.org/wiki/Environmental_ control_device

Eye gaze system	One of the earliest applications of eye-tracking was enabling computer access for the disabled. A device that pinpoints the gaze point on a computer screen can allow a quadriplegic to operate that computer by "pointing" with the gaze and "clicking" by blinking the eyelids or staring at a certain point on the screen for a length of time, thereby obtaining the functionality of a mouse. An on-screen keyboard and numeric keypad can allow for text typing and calculations, and continuous eye-movement tracking can allow the user to draw diagrams or create graphs. **http://whatis.techtarget.com/definition/eye-tracking-gaze-tracking**
EyeSpeak	EyeSpeak is the first autonomous system with an augmented reality interface by eye-tracking that will provide the possibility of communicating through the user's eyes in any position and orientation of the user's head. It will consist of a pair of augmented reality glasses that will project a virtual keyboard (or the display of the user's computer if it is connected to it) onto the user's field of view. Additionally, it will have a micro camera looking at the user's eyes to understand which key the user is selecting. After writing a word or set of words, the user will be able to select with his eyes the 'speak' button that will speak what the user has written in a synthetic voice through a speaker that is integrated into the glasses. Moreover, the user will be able to use his current computer by connecting the device to it and using his eyes to control the mouse. **http://www.lusovu.com/#/news**
Feeding syringes	A syringe used to deliver liquid formula or pureed foods into a feeding tube. It can be equipped with a plunger to push pureed food through the syringe and into the G-tube.
Feeding tube/ G-tube	A feeding tube, also called a gastrostomy tube or G-tube, is a medical device used to provide

nutrition to patients who cannot obtain nutrition by mouth, are unable to swallow safely, or need nutritional supplementation. The state of being fed by a feeding tube is called gavage, enteral feeding or tube feeding. Placement may be temporary for the treatment of acute conditions or lifelong in the case of chronic disabilities.
http://en.wikipedia.org/wiki/Feeding_tube

Flat polyp
...colon polyps come in two basic varieties: pedunculated and sessile. Pedunculated polyps are mushroom-like tissue growths that are attached to the surface of the mucous membrane by a long, thin stalk, or peduncle. Sessile polyps sit right on the surface of the mucous membrane. They do not have a stalk. Sessile polyps are flat.
http://coloncancer.about.com/od/colon cancerbasics/a/polyptypes.htm

Gastroenterologist
A physician trained in the practice of gastroenterology.

Gastroenterology
Referred to as GI, it is a branch of medicine concerned with the structure, functions, diseases, and pathology of the stomach and intestines.
http://www.merriam-webster.com/ dictionary/gastroenterology

Generator (portable)
A portable generator is a gas or diesel-powered device which provides temporary electrical power. The engine turns a small turbine, which in turn creates usable electricity up to a certain level of wattage. Users can plug electrical appliance or tools directly into the generator's sockets, or the generator can be professionally wired into the sub-panel of a home. **http://www.wisegeek.com/what-is-a-portable-generator.htm**

Google Glass
Google Glass is a type of wearable technology with an optical head-mounted display

(OHMD). It was developed by Google with the mission of producing a mass-market ubiquitous computer. Google Glass displays information in a smartphone-like hands-free format. Wearers communicate with the Internet via natural language voice commands. **http://en.wikipedia.org/wiki/Google_Glass**

Handicap van   Wheelchair-accessible van. A wheelchair-accessible van is a vehicle in a range of them that have been modified to increase the interior size of the vehicle and to equip it with a means of wheelchair entry such as a wheelchair ramp or powered lift, to allow access. **http://en.wikipedia.org/wiki/Wheelchair _accessible_van**

Home Health Nurse   A nurse who is responsible for a group of clients in the home setting. Visits clients on a routine basis to assist client and family with care as needed and to teach family the care needed so that the client may remain at home. Synonym(s): visiting nurse. **http://medical-dictionary.thefreedictionary.com/home+heal th+nurse**

Hoyer lift   See Patient lift.

Hyperventilation   Abnormally fast or deep respiration resulting in the loss of carbon dioxide from the blood, thereby causing a decrease in blood pressure and sometimes fainting. **http://medical-dictionary.thefreedictionary.com/hyperventi lation**

Hypoventilation   In medicine, hypoventilation (also known as respiratory depression) occurs when ventilation is inadequate (hypo meaning *below*) to perform needed gas exchange. By definition it causes an increased concentration of carbon dioxide (hypercapnia) and respiratory acidosis. **http://en.wikipedia.org/ wiki/Hypoventilation**

Invasive surgery	A form of surgery that involves making an incision in the patient's body and inserting instruments or other medical devices into it. **http://medical-dictionary.thefreedictionary.com/Invasive+surgery**
IV	Intravenous. Intravenous therapy (IV therapy) is the infusion of liquid substances directly into a vein. Intravenous simply means "within vein." Therapies administered intravenously are often called specialty pharmaceuticals. It is commonly referred to as a drip because many systems of administration employ a drip chamber, which prevents air from entering the blood stream (air embolism), and allows an estimation of flow rate. **http://en.wikipedia.org/wiki/Intravenous_therapy**
Kickstarter	According to its website, Kickstarter is the world's largest funding platform for creative projects. A home for film, music, art, theater, games, comics, design, photography, and more. Project creators set a funding goal and deadline. If people like a project, they can pledge money to make it happen. Funding on Kickstarter is all-or-nothing—projects must reach their funding goals to receive any money. To date, an impressive 44% of projects have reached their funding goals. **https://www.kickstarter.com/hello**
L.V.N.	Licensed Practical Nurse (licensed vocational nurse). A graduate of a school of practical nursing whose qualifications have been examined by a state board of nursing and who has been legally authorized to practice as a licensed practical or vocational nurse (L.P.N. or L.V.N.). **http://medical-dictionary.thefreedictionary.com/LVN**
Laparoscopic surgery	Laparoscopic surgery, also called minimally invasive surgery (MIS), bandaid surgery, or

keyhole surgery, is a modern surgical technique in which operations are performed far from their location through small incisions (usually 0.5-1.5 cm) elsewhere in the body. There are a number of advantages to the patient with laparoscopic surgery versus the more common, open procedure. Pain and hemorrhaging are reduced due to smaller incisions and recovery times are shorter. The key element in laparoscopic surgery is the use of a laparoscope, a long fiber optic cable system which allows viewing of the affected area by snaking the cable from a more distant, but more easily accessible location. **http://en.wikipedia.org/wiki/Laparoscopic_ surgery**

Locked-in syndrome   Locked-in syndrome (LIS) is a condition in which a patient is aware but cannot move or communicate verbally due to complete paralysis of nearly all voluntary muscles in the body except for the eyes. Total locked-in syndrome is a version of locked-in syndrome wherein the eyes are paralyzed as well. **http://en.wikipedia.org/wiki/Locked-in_syndrome**

Lou Gehrig's Disease   Amyotrophic Lateral Sclerosis (ALS). In the United States, ALS is often called Lou Gehrig's disease after the famous Yankee's baseball player, who died of the disease at the age of 37.

Malignancy   Malignancy (from Latin male, meaning "badly", and -gnus, meaning "born") is the tendency of a medical condition to become progressively worse. Malignancy is most familiar as a characterization of cancer. A malignant tumor contrasts with a non-cancerous benign tumor in that a malignancy is not self-limited in its growth, is capable of invading into adjacent tissues, and may be capable of spreading to distant tissues. A benign tumor has none of those properties. **http://en.wikipedia.org/wiki/Malignancy**

MODDERN Cures Act

Modernizing Our Drug & Diagnostics Evaluation and Regulatory Network Cures Act of 2013 or MODDERN Cures Act of 2013. Requires the Secretary of Health and Human Services (HHS) to: (1) establish the Advanced Diagnostics Education Council to recommend standard terms and definitions related to innovative diagnostics for use by patients, physicians, health care providers, payers, and policy makers; and (2) publish a guide regarding such terms and definitions. Sets forth additional factors for the Secretary to consider in determining the payment amount for new clinical diagnostic laboratory tests under gap filling procedures which are used when no comparable existing test is available. Extends the exclusivity period for a medicine if the diagnostic test related to such drug has been determined by the Secretary to have been developed by, or with the participation of, the manufacturer or sponsor of the medicine, and use of the diagnostic tests provides for or improves: (1) the identification of a patient population for the medicine; or (2) the determination of the most appropriate treatment option for a patient population with the medicine. Establishes a dormant therapy designation for medicine that addresses unmet medical needs. Gives such medicine 15 years of data exclusivity under which no drug can be approved by relying on the approval or licensure of the dormant therapy. Directs the Secretary to arrange with the Institute of Medicine to study intellectual property laws and their impact on therapy and diagnostic development in order to formulate recommendations on how to facilitate the clinical evaluation and development of therapies

	currently available on the market for new potential indications. **https://www.govtrack.us/congress/bills/113/hr3116#summary/libraryofcongress**
Morphine	Morphine (INN), which is sold under nearly a hundred trade names, is an opioid analgesic drug, and the main psychoactive chemical in opium. In clinical medicine, morphine is regarded as the gold standard of analgesics used to relieve intense pain. Like other opioids, such as oxycodone, hydromorphone, and diacetylmorphine (heroin), morphine acts directly on the central nervous system (CNS) to relieve pain. **http://en.wikipedia.org/wiki/Morphine**
Muscle biopsy	In medicine, a muscle biopsy is a procedure in which a piece of muscle tissue is removed from an organism and examined microscopically. A muscle biopsy can lead to the discovery of problems with a nervous system, connective tissue, vascular system, or musculoskeletal system. **http://en.wikipedia.org/wiki/Muscle_biopsy**
National ALS Registry	The National ALS Registry is a congressionally mandated registry for persons in the U.S. with ALS. It is the only population-based registry in the U.S. that collects information to help scientists learn more about who gets ALS and its causes. **https://wwwn.cdc.gov/als/Default.aspx_**
Neurologist	A neurologist is a physician specializing in neurology and trained to investigate, or diagnose and treat neurological disorders. Neurologists may also be involved in clinical research, and clinical trials, as well as basic research and translational research. **http://en.wikipedia.org/wiki/Neurology**
Neurology	Neurology neuron, and the suffix -logia (study of} is a medical specialty dealing with

disorders of the nervous system. To be specific, neurology deals with the diagnosis and treatment of all categories of conditions and disease involving the central and peripheral nervous system; or, the equivalent meaning, the autonomic nervous systems and the somatic nervous systems, including their coverings, blood vessels, and all effector tissue, such as muscle.
http://en.wikipedia.org/wiki/Neurology

Neuromuscular Registry

Neuromuscular diseases are those that affect the muscles and/or their direct nervous system control. In general, problems with central (or upper motor neuron) nervous control can cause either spasticity (from upper motor neuron conditions) or some degree of paralysis (from both lower and upper motor neuron disorders, upper motor neuron conditions usually being associated with concurrent hyperreflexia), depending on the location and the nature of the problem. A large proportion of neurological disorders leads to problems with movement. Some examples of central (or upper motor neuron) disorders include cerebrovascular accident (stroke), Parkinson's disease, multiple sclerosis, Huntington's disease (Huntington's chorea) and Creutzfeldt-Jakob disease. Spinal muscular atrophies are disorders of lower motor neuron while amyotrophic lateral sclerosis is a mixed upper and lower motor neuron condition. Neuropathies involve dysfunction of the peripheral nerves, which consist of: motor neurons that carry the electrical signals directly from the spinal cord and brain stem to activate muscle movement; the sensory neurons which convey sensory information such as pain, temperature, light touch, vibration and position to the brain; and the autonomic neurons which go to the internal organs and control blood vessel reflexes.

	Myasthenia gravis and Lambert-Eaton syndrome are examples of neuromuscular junction disorders. Muscular dystrophies and inflammatory myopathies such as polymyositis are examples of primary muscular (myopathic) disorders. **http://en.wikipedia.org/wiki/Neuromuscular_disease**
Nitroglycerine	Nitroglycerin is an antianginal, antihypertensive, and vasodilator used for the prophylaxis and treatment of angina pectoris, the treatment of congestive heart failure and myocardial infarction, and blood pressure control or controlled hypotension during surgery. **http://medical-dictionary.thefreedictionary.dictionary.com/nitroglycerin**
Otolaryngologist	Otolaryngologist is a physician who specializes in diagnosing and treating diseases of the head and neck, especially those involving the ears, nose, and throat (ENT). Also called an ENT, ENT doctor, or ENT physician. **http://www.medterms.com/script/main/art.asp?articlekey=4697**
PALS	Person with ALS.
Passy-Muir valve	Invented by a patient named David Muir, the Passy-Muir® Tracheostomy & Ventilator Swallowing and Speaking Valve is a simple medical device used by tracheostomy and ventilator patients. When placed on the hub of the tracheostomy tube or in-line with the ventilator circuit, the Passy-Muir Valve redirects air flow through the vocal folds, mouth and nose enabling voice and improved communication. **http://www.passy-muir.com/**
Patient lift	A patient lift (patient hoist, jack hoist, hydraulic lift) may be either a sling lift (or Hoyer Lift, a brand name) or sit-to-stand lift.

This is an assistive device that allows patients in hospitals and nursing homes and those receiving home health care to be transferred between a bed and a chair or other similar resting places, using hydraulic power. Sling lifts are used for patients whose mobility is limited. They could be mobile (or floor) lifts or overhead lifts (suspended from ceiling-mounted or overhead tracks).The sit-to-stand lift is designed to help patients who have some mobility but who lack the strength or muscle control to rise to a standing position from a bed, wheelchair, chair, or commode. They use straps, vests, or belts (as opposed to slings) to make the transition possible.
http://en.wikipedia.org/wiki/Patient_lift

pH

In chemistry, pH…is a measure of the acidity or basicity of an aqueous solution. Solutions with a pH less than 7 are said to be acidic and solutions with a pH greater than 7 are basic or alkaline. Pure water has a pH very close to 7.
http://en.wikipedia.org/wiki/PH

Phlebotomist

A person who draws blood for diagnostic tests or to remove blood for treatment purposes.
http://www.medterms.com/script/main/art.asp?articlekey=4876

Post-Polio Syndrome

Post-polio syndrome (PPS) is a condition that affects polio survivors years after recovery from an initial acute attack of the poliomyelitis virus. Most often, polio survivors start to experience gradual new weakening in muscles that were previously affected by the polio infection. The most common symptoms include slowly progressive muscle weakness, fatigue (both generalized and muscular), and a gradual decrease in the size of muscles (muscle atrophy). Pain from joint degeneration and increasing skeletal deformities such as scoliosis (curvature of the spine) is common and may precede the weakness and muscle

atrophy. Some individuals experience only minor symptoms while others develop visible muscle weakness and atrophy. Post-polio syndrome is rarely life-threatening, but the symptoms can significantly interfere with an individual's ability to function independently. Respiratory muscle weakness, for instance, can result in trouble with proper breathing, affecting daytime functions and sleep. Weakness in swallowing muscles can result in aspiration of food and liquids into the lungs and lead to pneumonia.
http://www.ninds.nih.gov/disorders/ post_polio/detail_post_polio.htm

Pressure sore   Bedsores, also called pressure sores or pressure ulcers, are injuries to skin and underlying tissue resulting from prolonged pressure on the skin. Bedsores most often develop on skin that covers bony areas of the body, such as the heels, ankles, hips and tailbone. People most at risk of bedsores are those with a medical condition that limits their ability to change positions, requires them to use a wheelchair or confines them to a bed for a long time.
http://www.mayoclinic.org/diseases- conditions/bedsores/basics/definition /con-20030848

Private duty nurse   Private nurse (private duty nurse) is one who attends an individual patient, usually on a fee-for-service basis, and who may specialize in a specific class of diseases.   **http://medical-dictionary.thefreedictionary.com/LVN**

Pulmonologist   A pulmonologist, or pulmonary disease specialist, is a physician who possesses specialized knowledge and skill in the diagnosis and treatment of pulmonary (lung) conditions and diseases.
http://www.healthcommunities.com/copd/ what-is-pulmonary-specialist.shtml

R.N.	A registered nurse (RN) is a nurse who has graduated from a nursing program at a college or university and has passed a national licensing exam to obtain a nursing license. **http://en.wikipedia.org/wiki/Registered_ nurse**
Radiologist	Radiologists are medical doctors (MDs) or doctors of osteopathic medicine (DOs) who specialize in diagnosing and treating diseases and injuries using medical imaging techniques, such as x-rays, computed tomography (CT), magnetic resonance imaging (MRI), nuclear medicine, positron emission tomography (PET) and ultrasound. **http://www.acr.org/Quality-Safety/ Radiology-Safety/Patient-Resources/About-Radiology**
Range of motion exercises	Range of motion (ROM) exercises are ones in which a nurse or patient move each joint through as full a range as is possible without causing pain. **http://www.brooksidepress.org/Products/ Nursing_Fundamentals_1/lesson_5_Section_ 1.htm**
Resection of colon	Large bowel resection is surgery to remove all or part of your large bowel. This surgery is also called colectomy. The large bowel is also called the large intestine or colon. Removal of the entire colon and the rectum is called a proctocolectomy. Removal of part or all of the colon but not the rectum is called subtotal colectomy. The large bowel connects the small intestine to the anus. Normally, stool passes through the large bowel before leaving the body through the anus. **http://www.nlm. nih.gov/medlineplus/ency/article/002941.htm**
Respiratory Therapist	A Respiratory Therapist is a specialized healthcare practitioner who has graduated from a university and passed a national board

certifying examination. Respiratory therapists work most often in intensive care and operating rooms, but are also commonly found in outpatient clinics and home-health environments. Respiratory therapists are specialists and educators in cardiology and pulmonology. Respiratory therapists are also advanced-practice clinicians in airway management; establishing and maintaining the airway during management of trauma, intensive care, and may administer anaesthesia for surgery or conscious sedation. **http://en.wikipedia.org/wiki/Respiratory_the rapy**

RoboRoach

The RoboRoach is available for purchase on the Internet as an educational do-it-yourself kit of a cockroach cyborg (a living organic being that has abiotic [nonliving] artificial parts). According to the Backyard Brains website, the kit includes a printed circuit board (the backpack), which carries a Bluetooth Low Energy wireless receiver/transmitter (so the user can communicate to it via a smartphone), a few indicator LEDs, and other circuit components. It also includes three sets of electrodes to implant three adult cockroaches. One end of each electrode set is a connector to plug in the RoboRoach backpack and the other end is a 0.003" silver wire (smaller than the thickness of a strand of hair) that serves as the conductive electrical element that interfaces with the sensory nerves of the cockroach. **https://backyardbrains.com/experiments/rob oRoachSurgery**

Sodium bicarbonate

A white crystalline weakly alkaline salt NaHCO3 used in baking powders and in medicine especially as an antacid—called also baking soda, bicarb, bicarbonate of soda, sodium acid carbonate.

http://www.merrium-webster.com/
medical/sodium%20bicarbinate

Speech Generating Devices

Speech-generating devices (SGDs), also known as voice output communication aids, are electronic augmentative and alternative communication (AAC) systems used to supplement or replace speech or writing for individuals with severe speech impairments, enabling them to verbally communicate their needs. SGDs are important for people who have limited means of interacting verbally, as they allow individuals to become active participants in communication interactions. Speech generating devices can produce electronic voice output by using digitized recordings of natural speech or through speech synthesis, which may carry less emotional information but can permit the user to speak novel messages.

http://en.wikipedia.org/wiki/Speech-generating_device

Staph infection

Staph infections are caused by staphylococcus bacteria, types of germs commonly found on the skin or in the nose of even healthy individuals. Most of the time, these bacteria cause no problems or result in relatively minor skin infections. But staph infections can turn deadly if the bacteria invade deeper into the body, entering the bloodstream, joints, bones, lungs or heart. A growing number of otherwise healthy people are developing life-threatening staph infections. Treatment usually involves antibiotics and drainage of the infected area. However, some staph infections no longer respond to common antibiotics.

http://www.mayoclinic.org/diseases-conditions/staph-infections/basics/definition/con-20031418

Stoma

A stoma (plural stomata) is an opening, either natural or surgically created, which connects a

	portion of the body cavity to the outside environment. http://en.wikipedia.org/wiki/Stoma_(medic ine)
Stroke	A stroke occurs when the blood supply to part of the brain is interrupted or severely reduced, depriving brain tissue of oxygen and food. Within minutes, brain cells begin to die. A stroke is a medical emergency. Prompt treatment is crucial. Early action can minimize brain damage and potential complications. http://www.mayoclinic.org/diseases-conditions/stroke/basics/definition/con-20042884
Suction catheter	Suction catheters are long flexible tubes that are used with a suction machine to remove fluids from the mouth and airways of people who have difficulty with swallowing or coughing. The plastic, rigid Yankauer suction tip is one type of tip attached to a suction unit. Another is the plastic, nonrigid French or whistle tip catheter. http://en.wikipedia.org/wiki/Suction_(medicine)
Suction machine	Suction machines are...electric suction units which contain a vacuum pump (piston, diaphragm, or rotary vane), bacterial filter, vacuum gauge, trap for moisture (or any debris accidentally drawn into the mechanism), a reservoir for the aspirated material, and a suction catheter or nozzle. They may be intended to provide high or low vacuum, and high and low flow rates. Low vacuum is used for post-operative wound drainage. http://home.btconnect.com/MalcolmBrown/entries/SUCTION_MACHINE.html
Suctioning	Suction may be used to clear the airway of blood, saliva, vomit, or other secretions so that

a patient may breathe. Suctioning can prevent pulmonary aspiration, which can lead to lung infections. In pulmonary hygiene, suction is used to remove fluids from the airways, to facilitate breathing and prevent growth of microorganisms.   **http://en.wikipedia.org/ wiki/Suction_(medicine)**

Trach

Trach (pronounced 'trake') refers to both tracheotomy, which is the surgical procedure of creating a stoma into the trachea to allow artificial breathing, and tracheostomy, which is the hole or opening created after the procedure. A tube may be inserted into the opening for support and is called a trach tube. **http://www.biology-online.org/dictionary /Trach**

Trachea

A tube-like portion of the respiratory tract that connects the larynx with the bronchial parts of the lungs. Also known as windpipe. **http://www.medterms.com/script/main/art.as p?articlekey=5829**

Tracheostomy tube

Tracheostomy tube: A small metal or plastic tube that keeps the stoma (opening) and the trachea in a tracheostomy open. Also known as a trach (pronounced 'trake') tube. **http://www.medterms.com/script/main/art.as p?articlekey=5833**

Trackball

A trackball is a pointing device consisting of a ball held by a socket containing sensors to detect a rotation of the ball about two axes— like an upside-down mouse with an exposed protruding ball. The user rolls the ball with the thumb, fingers, or the palm of the hand to move a pointer. **http://en.wikipedia.org/wiki/Trackball**

Ventilator

A medical ventilator is a machine designed to mechanically move breathable air into and out of the lungs, to provide the mechanism of breathing for a patient who is physically unable to breathe, or breathing insufficiently. **http://en.wikipedia.org/wiki/Medical_ventil ator**

Ventilator circuit

Ventilator circuits are tubes of various types which are used with medical ventilators. The patient circuit usually consists of a set of three durable, yet lightweight plastic tubes, separated by function (e.g. inhaled air, patient pressure, exhaled air). Determined by the type of ventilation needed, the patient-end of the circuit may be either noninvasive or invasive. Noninvasive methods, which are adequate for patients who require a ventilator only while sleeping and resting, mainly employ a nasal mask. Invasive methods require intubation, which for long-term ventilator dependence will normally be a tracheotomy cannula, as this is much more comfortable and practical for long-term care than is larynx or nasal intubation **http://en.wikipedia.org/wiki/Medical_venit lator**

Virtual keyboard

A virtual keyboard is a computer keyboard that a user operates by typing on or within a wireless- or optical-detectable surface or area rather than by depressing physical keys. Such a system can enable the user of a small handheld device, such as a cellular telephone or a PDA (personal digital assistant) to have full keyboard capability. In one technology, the keyboard is projected optically on a flat surface and, as the user touches the image of a key, the optical device detects the stroke and sends it to the computer. In another technology, the keyboard is projected on an area and selected keys are transmitted as wireless signals using the short-range Bluetooth technology. Theoretically, with either approach, the keyboard could even be projected in space and the user could type by moving fingers through the air. **http://whatis.techtarget.com/definition/virtu al-keyboard** .

Voice/Speech Synthesizer

Voice synthesizer is an electronic device that combines basic sounds to imitate the speech of a person. **http://www.yourdictionary.com/ voice-synthesizer**

Speech synthesis is the artificial production of human speech. A computer system used for this purpose is called a speech synthesizer, and can be implemented in software or hardware products. A text-to-speech (TTS) system converts normal language text into speech; other systems render symbolic linguistic representations like phonetic transcriptions into speech. **http://en.wikipedia.org/wiki/Speech_ synthesis**

Wound care specialist

A wound care specialist is a healthcare provider who focuses on evaluating and treating non-healing wounds. **http://www.healtogether.com/what-is-a-wound-care-specialist/**

Appendix C
Deciding Whether to Use a Ventilator

Ismail's journey with ALS, including living for twenty-four years at home on a portable ventilator, illustrates that a happy and productive life is possible on a ventilator. Such a life, however, is not for everybody.

Deciding whether to have a tracheotomy and use a ventilator is a complex and personal decision. If you are making that decision, you and your family must determine what would be best for you. The decision you make should be a thoughtful and informed one.

Living on a ventilator is costly. Not only is the equipment expensive, but the cost of home care assistance to provide support to family caregivers can be prohibitive. You and your family should check into what resources you have available to pay for the required equipment and ongoing care you will need.

If you are able to work at the time you begin using a ventilator, you most likely will be able to continue to work after your tracheotomy. If you are able to talk, you should be able to continue doing so. A special one-way "talking" valve called a Passy-Muir valve can be connected to your trach tube to help make talking easier. If your general physical condition allows you to safely swallow food, you may be able to continue to eat by mouth as well. You can remain mobile and, with careful planning, you can travel, too.

Should you decide to extend your life by using a ventilator, you should put an Advance Directive in place specifying your end-of-life decisions and instructions and under what conditions you would want to stop using the ventilator.

If you decide against using a ventilator, medications are available that can help relieve respiratory distress.

It's important for you to consider your options in advance, and the pros and cons of each. You and your family should make your decision before you actually need to use a ventilator.

In making your decision, be sure to consider:

1. Your condition and prognosis
2. Your options and the pros and cons of each
3. The resources you would need for each alternative
4. Which resources are available to you
5. The impact each alternative would have on you and your family over the long haul
6. Information about advanced directives
7. Other ways you can ensure that your decision will be known and that your wishes will be carried out.

Develop a Plan/Strategy:

1. Include your family and other people who are important to you in your decision-making process
2. Seek the advice of professionals who have actually had experience with patients who use a ventilator at home
3. Consider whether using home equipment such as a CPAP or BiPAP machine on a trial basis might be helpful
4. Avoid making a decision based on an initial emotional reaction
5. Avoid denial and procrastination
6. Try to find people with conditions similar to your own who are using ventilators at home. They and their families may be able to give you the best information

Source: *It's Your Choice*, video tape written and produced by Ismail and Cheryl Tsieprati, © 1991

For additional information:

Additional information that can be helpful to you in making your decision can be found in *Exploring the Option of a Trach*, written by Linda L. Bienick, Certified Employee Assistance Professional (retired), Advisory Board Member, International Ventilator Users Network (IVUN). You can access this article on the Internet at **http://www.ventusers.org/edu/ExploringOption Trach6032010.pdf**

Appendix D
Duties Performed by Ismail's Nurses

- Bathing (standard bed bath, including applying lotions and powders as necessary)
- Checking Ismail's body for red areas or skin breakdown
- Wound care as necessary, following doctor's and wound specialist's orders
- Gentle range of motion exercises
- Dressing Ismail
- Shaving Ismail
- Washing Ismail's hair
- Trach and G-tube care
- Giving Ismail his medications and vitamins according to schedule
- Preparing meals, pureeing them, and giving G-tube feedings to Ismail
- Transferring Ismail to and from his bed, his commode, and his wheelchair using the Hoyer lift
- Positioning Ismail properly in front of the television set
- Operating the television, DVD, and VCR equipment
- Assisting Ismail in finding television programs or DVD movies to watch, getting them running, changing channels for Ismail
- Administering Ismail's bowel program every other day
- Sterilizing water for suctioning by boiling it for 10 minutes and storing it in sterilized bottles
- Washing and changing bed linens
- Doing Ismail's laundry
- Setting up ventilator equipment; cleaning pieces of equipment that must be changed every day

- Ordering ventilator supplies and other home care supplies
- Repositioning Ismail throughout the day as needed for comfort and pressure release
- Helping Ismail use the urinal from time to time throughout the day
- Grinding up raw sunflower seeds and filtering the ground seeds through a strainer to create a powder that can be dissolved in liquid feedings
- Following up with questions for Ismail's doctor; obtaining needed doctors' orders
- Charging Ismail's wheelchair battery and back up batteries
- Undressing Ismail and preparing him for bed
- Brushing Ismail's teeth and doing oral care
- Positioning Ismail in bed at night and preparing him to go to sleep

Appendix E
Ismail's Daily Menu, Cheryl's Soup Recipe, and Vitamin Supplements

Important Note from Ismail: My personal diet and the supplemental vitamins I take are beneficial to me, and I believe they have helped to keep me healthy over the years. Of course, everyone has different needs. It is important that each person discuss their diet with their own doctor, who can advise him or her of the benefits and/or risks of making any dietary changes or taking vitamin supplements. I am in no way suggesting that anyone follow the same diet or take the same vitamins as I do!

Ismail's Daily Menu

For those who are interested in knowing what I am fed through my G-tube, here is a sample of my typical day's meals, all of which are pureed in a blender:

Breakfast:
- 1 can Glucerna liquid formula with fiber
- 1 hardboiled egg or 2 cooked egg whites
- ½ avocado
- ½ cup ground raw sunflower seeds
- ¼ cup protein powder

Lunch:
- 1 can Glucerna liquid formula with fiber
- Fresh fruit of choice
- 3 ounces cooked chicken breast
- 2 scoops of ground raw sunflower seeds

Dinner:
- Homemade soup - The recipe for Cheryl's soup is below
- 1 tablespoon olive oil

Cheryl's Meat and Vegetable Soup Recipe

- 4-5 pounds of skinned chicken breast or other lean meat or fish
- 1 small or ½ large cauliflower, chopped
- 12 Brussels sprouts or 4 cups broccoli, chopped
- 1 large bunch fresh kale, chopped
- 2 large green or red bell peppers, chopped
- 1 package sliced mushrooms
- ½ to 1 package frozen sliced okra
- ½ to 1 package frozen shelled soy beans, if desired
- 1-2 cans garbanzo beans, if desired
- 1-2 cans white beans, if desired
- ½ pound fresh or 2 cans of green beans
- 6-8 cups fresh spinach, thoroughly washed
- ½ cup uncooked brown rice
- Extra virgin olive oil
- Salt-free garlic seasoning mix
- Low salt chicken stock

Trim fat, if any, off of meat, chicken or fish. Cut into cubes and brown in olive oil in a large pressure cooker or other pot. Sprinkle with salt-free garlic seasoning mix and stir. Once browned, remove meat from pot and place in a bowl. Add more olive oil and brown all vegetables except spinach. Add more salt-free garlic seasoning mix to taste. Once vegetables have softened and cooked down, add spinach and cover pot. Cook until spinach is soft. Stir all vegetables. Add rice on top of vegetables. Pour in enough chicken stock to cover all. Add browned meat or fish on top of vegetables and rice. Add a little more stock until meat is nearly covered with stock. Close pot and cook until done. If using a pressure cooker, cook about 20 minutes once maximum pressure level is reached. Wait for soup to cool and stir well. Store in plastic containers and freeze until use.

Ismail's Supplemental Vitamins

- Multivitamin with 27 mg iron from Ferrous Sulfate
- Vitamin E - 400 iu
- Vitamin C - 500 mg
- Vitamin D3 - 100 iu
- Vitamin B1 - 100 mg
- Vitamin B2 - 100 mg
- Zinc - 50 mg
- Enteric Coated Omega 3 Fish Oil - 1200 mg (2 capsules per day)

Appendix F
Some of Ismail's Favorite Things

Cheryl:
> Ismail's best friend and partner in all things

Westerns:
> *High Noon*
> *Gunfight at the O.K. Corral*
> *Man Without a Star*
> *Tombstone with Ken Russell*
> *Shane*
> *Rio Bravo*
> *El Dorado*
> *Stagecoach with John Wayne*
> *Destry*
> *Destry Rides Again*
> *The Good, The Bad, and the Ugly*

Western Actors:
> Kirk Douglas
> John Wayne
> Gary Cooper
> James Stewart
> Audie Murphy
> Randolph Scott
> James Garner
> Clint Eastwood

Food Channel:
> Guy Fieri's *Diners, Drive-Ins, and Dives*

Animals:
> Elephants
> Tropical birds
> Giraffes

Color:

   Yellow

Operas:

   La Traviata by Verdi

   Carmen by Georges Bizet

Classical Music:

   Franz Schubert: *Ave Maria, Unfinished Symphony,* and *The Trout*

   Johann Sebastian Bach: *Brandenburg Concertos*

   Ludwig Van Beethoven: *Fur Elise and Fifth Symphony*

Musical Comedies:

   Singing in the Rain

   My Fair Lady

   Oklahoma

   Fiddler On the Roof

   Bandwagon

Singers:

   Mario Lanza

   Luciano Pavarotti

   Placido Domingo

   Jose Carreras

   Beverly Sills

   Regina Resnik

   Andrea Bocelli

   Perry Como

   Dean Martin

   Frank Sinatra

   Harry Belafonte

   Nat King Cole

   Elvis Presley

   Frankie Avalon

   Connie Francis

   Sting

   Billy Joel

Elton John
Simon and Garfunkel
Beyonce

Authors:
Lord Byron
Charles Dickens
Leo Tolstoy
Ivan Turgenev
Honore' de Balzac
Emile Zola
Nikolai Gogol
Johann Wolfgang von Goethe
Victor Hugo
Herman Melville
Jack London
Edgar Allan Poe

Foreign Country:
Italy, especially Venice

Appendix G
Resources

Note: Following is list of resources that we have found helpful during our journey with ALS. We realize that everyone's journey and needs are different and that resources we have found helpful might not necessarily be appropriate for or helpful to others.

The Internet can be the most valuable resource of all. With a few keywords typed into an Internet search engine, you can find information about nearly everything. To get the most from your Internet searches you will need to know the right keywords to use and appropriate questions to ask. We hope the list below will give you ideas to explore. Of course, you need to use your discretion to ensure that any information you get on the Internet is accurate and is obtained from reliable sources. We wish the Internet existed when Ismail was first diagnosed with ALS and when he started using the ventilator. The Internet would have made our journey easier.

Organizations Providing Services to the ALS Community

THE ALS ASSOCIATION
http://www.alsa.org/

Services Provided:

The Association leads the way in research, care services, public education, and public policy—giving help and hope to those facing the disease. The Association's nationwide network of chapters provides comprehensive patient services and support to the ALS community. The mission of the ALS Association is to lead the fight to treat and cure ALS through global research and nationwide advocacy, while also empowering people with Lou Gehrig's Disease and their families to live fuller lives by providing them with compassionate care and support.

National ALS Headquarters:

1275 K Street NW, Suite 250
Washington, DC 20005
phone: 202-407-8580
fax: 202-289-6801

Operations:

27001 Agoura Road, Suite 250
Calabasas Hills, CA 91301-5104
phone: 818-880-9007
fax: 818-880-9006

MUSCULAR DYSTROPHY ASSOCIATION (MDA)
http://mda.org/

Services Provided:
- Funds worldwide research
- Provides comprehensive health care services
- Provides support to MDA families nationwide
- Rallies communities to fight back through advocacy, fundraising and local engagement

General correspondence:

Muscular Dystrophy Association - USA
National Office
222 S. Riverside Plaza, Suite 1500
Chicago, Illinois 60606
Phone: (800) 572-1717
Email: mda@mdausa.org (link sends e-mail)
    To contact your local MDA office, use the website's office locator to find the phone number, email address and mailing address of the MDA office in your area.

Tips for Hiring Home Caregivers

Note: We have always used nurses who have been provided by nursing agencies. However, we are listing the following resources as examples of information that can be found on the Internet to assist families who are interested in hiring their own home caregivers.

AARP

http://www.aarp.org/relationships/caregiving-resource-center/info-08-2010/pc_home_care_worker.html

The website provides information on topics such as:
- Finding Candidates
- Considering Applicants
- Conducting an Interview
- Checking References

Available on the website:
- Video on Choosing an Agency for In-Home Care
- Video on Hiring a home care worker
- Article on How to assess your loved one's situation
- Article on Types of in-home care providers

CARE.COM

https://www.care.com/a/7-tips-for-hiring-a-live-in-special-needs-nurse-1306280159

The website provides information about seven steps to make the process for hiring a live-in special-needs nurse easier:
1. Decide if You Need a Caregiver or a Nurse
2. Figure Out What You Need
3. Know Where to Look
4. Interview Applicants
5. Ask About Lifestyle
6. Schedule a Trial Period
7. Have Patience

FAMILY CAREGIVER ALLIANCE (FCA)

National Center on Caregiving

https://caregiver.org/hiring-home-help

The website includes information on:
Assessing Your Home Care Needs:
- **Personal Care:** bathing, eating, dressing, toileting
- **Household Care:** cooking, cleaning, laundry, shopping
- **Health Care:** medication management, physician's appointments, physical therapy
- **Emotional Care:** companionship, meaningful activities, conversation

The website also includes links to:
- FCA Fact Sheet: *Making Choices About Everyday Care*
- FCA Fact Sheet: *Community Care Options*
- *Needs Assessment Worksheet from Family Care America*
- *Helping My Parents: How Do I Know If They Need Help from AARP*

The website provides tips on:
- Writing a job description
- Pros and cons of home care agencies
- Pros and cons of privately hired home care workers
- Developing a job contract
- Finding the right home care worker
- Locating resources in your community
- Interviewing the applicant
- What are the employer's responsibilities?
- Making your home care situation work
- Additional resources
- Organizations:
  - Family Caregiver Alliance
  - Children of Aging Parents
  - National Association for Home Care and Hospice (NAHC)
  - Visiting Nurses Association of America

Equipment Services

VENTILATORS & OTHER DURABLE MEDICAL EQUIPMENT:

APRIA HEALTHCARE
http://www.apria.com/wps/portal/apria/home
To speak with a customer service representative about services available in your area:

Phone: (800) 277-4288
Email: contact_us@apria.com

DME Services Provided:

Apria Healthcare provides a wide range of home medical equipment to help improve the quality of life for patients with special needs. Apria's homecare specialists talk to both the patient and the caregiver, evaluate the home environment and provide the appropriate equipment as directed by the doctor's treatment. Patients and their caregivers receive not only equipment, but caring support from our expert staff.

WHEELCHAIRS:
NATIONAL SEATING AND MOBILITY
http://www.nsm-seating.com/
National Corporate Office:
318 Seaboard Lane, Suite 202
Franklin, TN 37067
Phone: 615-595-1115 & 615-595-1750
Email: info@nsm-seating.com

Services Provided:

National Seating & Mobility's only business is custom mobility, Rehab and adaptive seating systems. During three decades, we've grown from five locations to a national network of professional Assistive Technology Providers (ATPs) serving clients, therapists and physicians across the U.S.

WHEELCHAIR ACCESSIBLE VANS:
MOBILITY WORKS
http://www.mobilityworks.com/
Sales: 877-275-4907
Service: 877-275-4912
Rentals: 877-275-4915

Services Provided:

MobilityWorks offers new and used wheelchair accessible vans to accommodate your specific needs from our 31 showrooms across the country.

Providing Mobility and Independence to Thousands of Physically Challenged Clients Each Year through Wheelchair Vans, Scooter Lifts, Hand Controls & the Latest in Adaptive Technology

Additional Resource

NON-CHEW COOKBOOK
By J. Randy Wilson
http://www.amazon.com/Non-Chew-Cookbook-J-Randy-Wilson/dp/0961629908

Acknowledgments

Thank you is not enough to express the deep gratitude we have for the many people who have assisted us with this book and who have given us their love, support, and encouragement along the way.

We are grateful to have family and friends who are always there to help us through the bad times and celebrate the good times. We love our wonderful brothers, sisters-in-law, nieces, nephews, grandnieces, and grandnephews who bring joy, comfort and laughter into our lives. We treasure each and every one of them.

We cherish the love and encouragement of our lifelong friends Phil and Jane Gries. Phil has been like a brother to Ismail for 52 years and Jane has been a supportive and nurturing friend for over 45 years. Phil is our biggest fan. He has encouraged us to complete this book and provided suggestions and resources to help us get it out to the world.

John and Sherry D'Attile are also more like family than friends. They have been at the center of our support system for more than fifty years. We are blessed to have these loving lifelong friends in our lives and cherish every day we spend with them and their family.

We thank all of the outstanding physicians over the years who have made an important difference in our lives and have kept Ismail strong and healthy. Special thanks to Dr. Edward Anthony Oppenheimer and Dr. Luis Moreta-Sainz, Pulmonology; Dr. Rebecca Hanson, Neurology; Dr. W King Engel, USC Neuromuscular Center; and Dr. Kevin Colwell, Family Medicine. There are many physicians and health care workers who have made a significant contribution to our health and our lives, and we are deeply grateful to them all.

Our deepest gratitude to all of the excellent nurses, present and past, who have taken outstanding care of Ismail

211

for the past 24 years. Some of our dedicated long-term nurses have been with us for more than ten years, a couple have been taking care of Ismail close to 20 years. We love them all and appreciate everything they do to keep Ismail healthy and happy.

We work with two wonderful nursing agencies that ensure that qualified nurses fill all of our nursing shifts every day and that Ismail receives the best of care. We appreciate all the hard work these agencies and their excellent staffs put in to recruiting new nurses, overseeing the quality of Ismail's care, and making certain our lives run as smoothly as possible.

Cathy Feldman of Blue Point Books has been a pleasure to work with. She has partnered with us throughout the editing, designing, and publishing process, providing excellent guidance and professional expertise and always ensuring superior quality.

Sarah Tuso did an amazing job as our first copy editor and as a proof reader. Her editorial expertise and keen insights helped to shape our first draft into a better book.

We are grateful to our early readers, Caz Cazanov, Trish Davidson, and Linda Rand, who provided valuable insight. Their observations, questions, and suggestions led to many improvements.

Our thanks to Judith Gerhart for her friendship and excellent financial advice over the years. We are grateful to Judith for introducing us to Cathy Feldman and for her encouragement throughout the publication process. Our thanks also to Judith's assistant Jill, always cheerful and charming and eager to help.

We appreciate all that Lynn Klein has done for us. She provided instrumental assistance during the production of our educational videos *It's Your Choice, Caring for the Caregiver,* and *What is ALS?* and has been helpful to us throughout the years. We treasure the photograph she took of Ismail with Stephen Hawking at the Peninsula Hotel.

We are grateful to Jackie Neff for providing help and support to us in difficult times and in good times. We cherish her friendship.

Wanda Buffington of At Wanda's has been coming to our home every few weeks for almost 20 years to cut and style Ismail's hair. We thank her for making our lives easier by providing these in-home services and for keeping Ismail nicely groomed.

We thank Martin Tajiboy for keeping Ismail's power wheelchair in good repair for nearly 20 years and for always brightening our day with his smile and sunny attitude.

Finally, we thank the ALS Association for all of its help and support over the years.

About the Authors

Ismail Tsieprati is a former film and video editor, producer, director, and writer with more than 25 years of experience in the film and video industry. He has written many screenplays and has extensive educational film credits. Ismail was presented with a special citation from the City of Los Angeles, Department of Building and Safety, for playing an instrumental role in the initial production of the Department's training video series. In 2003, Ismail was presented with the ALS March of Faces Vice President's *ALS Awareness and Advocacy Award* for his outstanding achievements in raising public awareness of ALS. Although he is totally paralyzed and no longer able to speak or write, Ismail communicates by blinking his eyes to spell out words and sentences. Using this method, he writes blog posts for social media and collaborates with Cheryl on musical theatre and other writing projects. He wrote chapters for this book by spelling out each word one blink at a time.

Cheryl Tsieprati worked in the health care industry for nearly 40 years. She has more than 25 years of experience in training consulting, instructional design, writing, and editing. As a freelance journalist, she received a first place award from the Associated Press, Western Region for her work on a newspaper series *Retailing in the '80s*. Cheryl also received an award for a comprehensive seminar she developed and facilitated for individuals with neuromuscular diseases and their family caregivers. She enjoys working on creative projects with Ismail, her husband of 44 years, being an ALS advocate, and collaborating on new musicals as book writer or lyricist.

Together, as co-owners of a video production company in the early 1990s, Cheryl and Ismail wrote and produced several promotional and educational videotapes, including *It's Your Choice*, a 26-minute educational video produced in 1991 which presents information and options to people facing respiratory failure. In 1993, Ismail and Cheryl wrote and produced *Caring for the Caregiver*, a 28-minute educational video with accompanying training materials for family caregivers, and *What is ALS?*, an informational video for the National ALS Association.

More Information About
One Blink at a Time

Individual copies of *One Blink at a Time* may be purchased by going to our website, **www.oneblinkatatime.com,** and clicking on the Amazon.com button. You can also go to **Amazon.com** and type *One Blink at a Time* in the search bar.

Volume discounts are available. We also offer a special fund-raising program for ALS chapters and other nonprofit groups. Please contact the publisher, Blue Point Books, at bpbooks@west.net or call 800-858-1058 for more information.

Discussion Guides to *One Blink at a Time* designed for Book Clubs and Support Groups are available as free downloads from our website: **www.oneblinkatatime.com**.

You can follow what's happening with Ismail and Cheryl on Facebook at **Ismail Tsieprati**.

If you are interested in having Cheryl Tsieprati speak at your conference, support group, or workshop, please address your inquiries to bpbooks@west.net or call 800-858-1058.

A portion of the proceeds from the sales of *One Blink at a Time* will be donated to the ALS Association.

Made in the USA
San Bernardino, CA
23 September 2016